UNDERSTANDING THE DRUG-EXPOSED CHILD

UNDERSTANDING
THE DRUG-EXPOSED CHILD

Approaches to Behavior and Learning

[handwritten inscription:] To Rob — With best wishes, Ira Chasnoff

Ira J. Chasnoff, M.D.
Amy R. Anson, Ph.D.
Kai A. Moss Iaukea, M.S.

Imprint Publications
Chicago

Library of Congress Catalog Card Number 98-70479
ISBN 1-879176-29-7 (Paper)

Printed in the United States of America on acid-free paper

Contents

The development of the book was supported by a grant to the National Association for Family Addiction Research and Education from the United States Department of Education, Safe and Drug Free Schools Program.

Introduction

The classroom is tense and silent as Eric throws down his books in frustration. It has become almost a daily occurrence, one that has left your classroom in chaos and your attempts at teaching in shambles. His previous teacher told you about Eric's prenatal exposure to drugs and about his outbursts, but as an experienced first grade teacher you were sure you could control his behavior. At the beginning of the year, he had been compliant and quiet, seldom participating, but seldom disturbing the classroom. Since winter break, however, his behavior has become uncontrollable, increasingly aggressive and impulsive, and punctuated by vocal outbursts. Attempts at physical restraint have been unsuccessful, but once he exhausts his energies, he sits quietly, often completing the task he was doing when the episode began.

You have repeatedly called his mother to come in for a conference, but she has never shown up. Recent attempts at communication with her have accomplished nothing. You certainly have tried everything in your book to help Eric, but his constant demands and acting out are causing you to neglect the other 25 children in the classroom. You feel angry and frustrated. What should you do now?

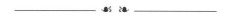

One of the greatest challenges teachers face today is the increasing number of children who do not respond to traditional instruction and classroom management techniques. Included in this category are children who were prenatally exposed to alcohol, cocaine, marijuana, and other drugs of abuse. In the past twenty years, we have learned more and more about these children and the lives of chaos and daily change many of them face. The difficulty has been translating this growing body of knowledge into practical information teachers can use in the classroom.

On top of this, during the past several years, the media have presented a provocative and bleak outcome for prenatally exposed children. They have been shown as having significant emotional and behavioral problems that interfere with their ability to profit from formalized instruction. The assumption has been that there always are residual effects of the drug, virtually assuring adjustment and academic problems. Consequently, schools across the country have felt unprepared to respond to what they believe will be the unique needs of prenatally exposed children.

Until now, no baseline of information has existed to confirm or refute these perceptions or to guide development of appropriate education plans and family outreach programs for children affected by prenatal drug exposure. Many reports from all over the country describe substance-exposed children, but most of them are misleading because of the difficulty of identifying the longstanding psychosocial issues in the history of the family, determining the pattern of prenatal drug exposure, and, finally, accounting for the environment in which the child is being raised. All these issues come together to produce children who are at risk for developmental or behavioral problems that disrupt the learning process and the classroom.

The National Association for Families and Addiction Research and Education (NAFARE) for the past twelve years has been studying the impact of prenatal drug exposure on children's long-term development. We now have research-based information that can guide schools and teachers in their efforts to address the needs of prenatally exposed children by developing appropriate interventions for behavioral problems. This research-based information is the foundation of this book.

This book is designed for teachers, parents, physicians, psychologists - for anyone who works with children. Often access to outside consultation and support is limited and in many (if not most) cases, you will not even know the child was exposed to drugs before birth. But the strategies we propose are appropriate for any child whose behavioral difficulties do not respond to standard interventions.

We know you are busy, so we have bridged the gap between research and practice with descriptive information, case strategies, and practical examples to get you started right away applying this material in the classroom. In developing the book, we made some assumptions:

- that teachers are in the classroom "on your own" and do not have ready access to help from psychologists or other specialists when behavioral problems arise;

- that a teacher is not a trained therapist or counselor ; we do not expect a teacher to adopt that role;

- that interventions in a classroom must be practical and easily used with a high degree of success; and

- that teachers wish to use strategies that reflect a "best practices" approach, i.e., that have been proved in research to be effective for behavioral problems.

We have arranged the content of the manual into three broad areas:

(1) the research basis of intervention strategies,

(2) principles of child behavior and classroom management, and

(3) guidelines for the development of individual behavioral interventions.

All information in the book is based on research studies conducted by NAFARE and other groups, and the intervention strategies have been piloted and field tested in a variety of situations, in both rural and urban school settings. Rather than a "cookbook" approach, we present the information in a way that takes the reader through a series of decision-making processes that can be incorporated into daily activities.

Throughout this book, we will ask you to shift your perceptions of the drug-exposed child from one who is willfully disobedient to one whose central nervous system may have been affected by drugs crossing the placenta during pregnancy. We will describe patterns of behavior exhibited by many of the drug-exposed children in our research studies, but we will caution you to remember that all children are unique and that there are a wide range of home and school factors that influence the behavior of any child. We will take a developmental approach in describing the impact of prenatal drug exposure on the long-term outcome of the child, starting in the newborn period and following the child through school age. Finally, we will use actual cases from our experience to provide an "anchor" to our learning approach.

Using the Book

This book will not help you specifically identify a prenatally exposed child, but it will enhance your ability to address the needs of any child demonstrating difficulties in the classroom. The book focuses on the prenatally exposed child because so little information exists about this population of children and because there appear to be some differences in the way the prenatally exposed child's behavioral difficulties need to be addressed. For the experienced teacher, this book may help you to sharpen current skills, refresh your memory, and present some information in a different way. For the beginning teacher, we hope you will develop a knowledge base that will help you become a more confident master of your classroom.

Three Themes for You to Consider

To assist you in learning and using the book, we have included examples and case studies. We suggest you read the entire book to gain a perspective of our approach and then return to Sections 2 and 3 to review specific concepts regarding interventions. We hope you will adopt our problem-solving approach so that when you encounter problems not covered in the book, you will have a strategy for developing an effective intervention. First, consider the classroom interventions described in Section 2, which may help solve the majority of your problems. For additional help, use Section 3 to develop interventions for the individual child displaying behavioral difficulties. As you read the book, we hope you will relate some of your past experiences to our approach and perhaps develop some new insights.

Now You Are Ready to Begin

The following themes are evident throughout the book and will help guide you through the material:

1. *Be proactive rather than reactive*
   In a proactive approach, planning and organization form the basis of the educational experience that aims to help children perform in the classroom. In a reactive approach, a problem occurs and an action is taken without carefully planning an effective method to address the problem. We are not saying situations do not arise that require immediate attention. However, long-term behavioral change is best accomplished through a proactive approach.

2. *Take a problem-solving approach*

   In this book, we take you through the problem-solving approach for finding solutions for children's behavioral problems, starting with classroom approaches and moving to individual, child-specific behavioral management strategies when necessary. As you become familiar with this approach, we believe you will be better able to describe the problems you see in specific terms and arrive at a practical, effective, and time efficient solution, applying the interventions in a confident and logical manner.

3. *Emphasize internal management over external control*

   Throughout this book, we emphasize that your goal should not be to control behavior by suppressing or eliminating it. Rather, it should be to teach children how to gain internal structuring and self-regulation capabilities. With appropriate interventions, children will learn better how to manage themselves and take responsibility for their behavior. By emphasizing management, we propose that you teach children behavior management skills just as you would teach subject material.

THE RESEARCH BASIS OF INTERVENTION STRATEGIES

The first National Education Goal states that "by the year 2000, all children in America will start school ready to learn." To achieve this goal, three objectives are outlined. The first objective targets disadvantaged and disabled children and ensures they will have access to high-quality and developmentally appropriate preschool programs. Expanding on that commitment, the second objective recognizes the critical role of parents in the development of their children: "every parent in America will be a child's first teacher and devote time each day to helping his or her preschool child learn; parents will have access to the training and support they need." The third objective specifies that "all children will receive the nutrition and health care needed to arrive at school with healthy minds and bodies, and that the number of low birth weight babies will be significantly reduced through prenatal health systems." Through these objectives, the needs of all children, particularly those who are at risk, have been made a priority by the U.S. Department of Education and educators throughout the nation.

Nothing interferes more with the realization of these national education goals, however, than the growing number of children affected by risk factors such as prenatal drug exposure, lack of adequate health care, and unsafe environments. During the critical early years of learning, these high-risk and vulnerable children often are not provided with the support and positive opportunities that enable them to develop the attitudes, skills, and behaviors essential for arriving at school "ready to learn" and continuing to be successful in school. Parents affected by substance abuse and a multitude of other risk factors also may not have the skills they need to guide their children's healthy development.

The most recent data from the National Institute on Drug Abuse (1994) suggest that up to 221,000 children per year are exposed to illicit drugs during gestation. The number of alcohol- and tobacco-exposed children far exceeds this figure, placing the total number of infants born each year prenatally exposed to alcohol, tobacco, and illicit drugs at well over 1.5 million. No data are available as to the number of exposed children who are now of preschool or school age, but state and local education agencies across the nation are reporting increasing numbers of high- risk and vulnerable prenatally exposed children who require special services and programs because of difficulties in school performance and participation.

Substance Abuse and the Family

Although inborn patterns or characteristics are important to a child's development, psychosocial and family factors can cause or contribute to success or failure in multiple areas of a child's life, including education. Systematic consideration of these factors is important in understanding child behavior in general and is particularly relevant to prenatally exposed children. Child growth and development are dynamic processes, involving both social and biological issues, with the biological issues being related to the direct impact of any particular drug on an unborn child's developing brain.

From a psychosocial perspective, the lifestyle of substance-abusing parents is filled with factors that tend to interfere with attempts at parenting, effective child rearing, and participation in the education of their children. These factors are present to some extent in all women who abuse drugs at a high level, regardless of socioeconomic status. Further, the social environment of many addicted women is one of chaos and instability, which has an even greater negative impact on children.

Addicted women frequently have poor family and social support networks, have few positive relationships with other women, and often are dependent on an unreliable, abusive male, thereby increasing their vulnerability to physical and sexual abuse. Children of substance abusing women are at greater risk for neglect and sexual, physical, and psychological abuse. These difficulties are magnified in children living in poverty, because their mothers frequently lack the social and economic supports that could help lessen some of the social isolation as well as the biological impact of prenatal drug exposure.

Significant psychiatric/psychological problems such as a personality disorder or mood disorders, especially depressive illnesses, are not uncommon in women who use drugs or abuse alcohol. These factors almost invariably impede parenting capabilities further and lessen the chance for a normal developmental course for the child. Even in non-substance-abusing depressed women, there is less involvement with their children, impaired communication among family members, increased friction, lack of affection, and an increase in guilt and resentment toward the child. To further complicate the picture, children of depressed mothers are significantly more likely to show depression than are children of non-depressed mothers. If there is a cyclical relationship between drug use and depression, i.e., drug use leads to depression, which leads to continued drug use, then the probability of transmission of the woman's depressive illness or substance use problems to her children increases.

For the teacher working with a child from a family with substance abuse problems, depression is an important consideration because depressed children tend to have academic and social problems to a greater extent than their peers. Only severe depression in children is detected in school settings, while milder forms tend to be overlooked or viewed as poor motivation. As a teacher evaluates a child, it is necessary to evaluate the child's needs within the context of the parenting capabilities and psychological functioning of the family, for overlying risk from substance abuse problems is the high rate of psychiatric problems among drug-using individuals.

Risk and Resiliency Factors for Prenatally Exposed Children

The healthy infant is born with sound neurodevelopmental functioning that is enhanced by life circumstances. However, as the child grows and develops, he or she is vulnerable to a variety of risk factors that can negatively affect long-term outcome. As the number of risk factors builds, risk for the child's ultimate outcome increases significantly (Sameroff, et al., 1984; Seifer and Sameroff, 1987). Protective factors modify the child's response to environmental hazards (Rutter,1985), and resiliency is the capacity to adapt after being exposed to stressful events (Werner, 1989). The child's inborn biological resilience or resilience developed through emotional and developmental support in the home allow the infant to meet challenges and overcome adversity.

This concept of the balance of risk and resiliency can guide our understanding of the biological and environmental factors that affect the drug-exposed child's development, but it cannot predict ultimate outcome of the child, since child development is an ongoing process shaped by multiple factors, many of which interact and influence one another in ways we cannot measure. However, intervention strategies that address multiple risk factors; provide support in a variety of settings; build their interventions on the cultural and ethnic foundations of the families they serve; work with the family and child for two to five years; initiate interventions as early as possible in the infants' lives; and combine interventions for both child and family have the greatest potential for positively affecting the outcome of the child (Yoshikawa, 1994). These tenets are the foundation upon which we have built our approach to working with children prenatally exposed to drugs.

Successful Intervention Strategies

• *build on the cultural and ethnic foundations of the families;*

• *work with the family and child for an extended period;*

• *initiate interventions as early as possible in the infants' lives; and*

• *combine interventions for both child and family.*

The Impact of Prenatal Drug Exposure on the Child

For teachers trying to work with the school-age prenatally-exposed child, it is important to have an appreciation of the child's status from a developmental perspective. Thus we will examine the impact of prenatal drug exposure through a progressive time frame, moving from the newborn period and early infancy to school age.

The Newborn and Young Infant: Medical Problems

Deficient growth patterns are among the most frequently cited problems occurring among substance-exposed newborns. As a group, average birth weight is significantly reduced in most studies. Although as the child grows older, average weight "catches up" to normal, low birth weight is a significant risk factor for developmental outcome as a child gets older.

Accompanying poor weight gain of the drug-exposed fetus is poor head growth, a reflection of poor intrauterine brain growth. Alcohol, cocaine, and heroin have been shown to be the three drugs most closely associated with poor brain growth. In general small head circumference at birth is a significant marker of risk for poor developmental outcome. In follow up of prenatally-exposed children, it has been shown that average head circumference does not reach the normal range until four to five years of age, and for some prenatally exposed children, head size continues to be smaller throughout early childhood. A child with a medical history or noted evidence of small head size in proportion to body size should alert the teacher to examine the child's developmental history, which may help to explain some difficulties in the classroom.

Because drug or alcohol-using women are more likely to smoke cigarettes, have infections complicating their pregnancy, and have inadequate prenatal care, and because cocaine in particular has a direct effect on the uterus, causing contractions, it is not surprising that there is a high rate of prematurity among prenatally-exposed infants. Premature delivery robs the fetus of the opportunity to reach full growth potential in the womb and places the child at increased risk for medical and developmental problems in the long term. Educationally, prematurity may show its effects in mild learning and behavioral problems. Again, however, because these children may live in a chaotic environment, it may be difficult to determine which effects are the result of prematurity, prenatal drug exposure, the environment, or a combination of all these factors.

Newborns and young infants who have been prenatally exposed to substances of abuse may suffer a range of physical and behavioral problems.

- *Fetal Alcohol Syndrome causes pre- and postnatal growth deficiency, central nervous system abnormalities, mental retardation and structural changes in the face and head (Jones, et al, 1973; Oulellette, et al, 1977).*

- *Infants prenatally exposed to heroin and methadone are typically irritable, tremulous, hypertonic and suffer from diarrhea and vomiting (Finnegan, et al, 1975).*

(continued on next page...)

• *Prenatal PCP exposure causes increased irritability, tremors and increased sensitivity to environmental stimuli (Chasnoff, et al, 1983).*

• *Cocaine use during pregnancy has been associated with low birth weight, prematurity, diminished body length and head circumference, congenital anomalies, and neurobehavioral deficiencies in the newborn period (Chasnoff, et al, 1985; Chasnoff, et al, 1989; Chavez, et al, 1989; Eisen, et al, 1991; Frank, et al, 1990; Lester, et al, 1991; Singer, et al, 1991).*

• *Infants prenatally exposed to drugs may be difficult to care for because of significant feeding and sleeping problems, hyperirritability, and hypersensitivity to touch, movement and eye contact. They may spend their time in bouts of inconsolable crying, being very irritable, or being unresponsive in a deep sleep (Griffith, 1988).*

• *A study of three month old infants who had been prenatally exposed to cocaine found the children's arousal and attention regulation were affected rather than early cognitive processes (Mayes, et al, 1995).*

Behavioral Problems

Prenatal exposure to drugs may interfere with a newborn's abilities to respond to the world around him. Newborn neurobehavior refers to the ability of infants to interact with their environment, to respond to stimuli as they occur, and to interact appropriately with the mother or other caretaker. Although physical difficulties in prenatally exposed infants occur in only about 25% to 30% of cases, neurobehavioral deficiencies are far more common.

The key areas of neurobehavior affected by prenatal substance exposure appear to be:

• **motor behavior** (reflexes, motor control, coordination of motor activities

- **orientation** (the infant's ability to respond to visual and auditory stimulation)

- **state control** (the infant's ability to regulate his behavior by moving appropriately through the various states of arousal - from sleep to awake to crying and irritable - and to calm himself in response to the demands of the environment)

Motor

The motor behaviors of substance-exposed infants can vary widely. The infants may be quite stiff, with rigid posturing and hyperextension of the trunk. They may have difficulty reaching, grabbing, exploring objects, and bringing their hands to the midline, and their reflexes may be hyperactive. On the other hand, quite a few of these infants are very limp and lethargic at birth, with poor response to handling. In either case, the abnormal motor behavior interferes with coordination of the suck and swallow response, and feeding difficulties are not uncommon. Alcohol, cocaine, PCP, and heroin have all been shown to affect motor behaviors of newborn infants.

Orientation

Prenatal substance exposure can affect the newborn's ability to respond to sound and to visual stimuli. Although the infant hears the sound, she has difficulty finding where the sound came from or showing attention to the sound. Visual stimuli have the same effect, with the child able to perceive that there is something to see but having difficulty focusing her gaze, even briefly, on the object. Children prenatally exposed to cocaine, heroin or PCP have difficulties with these orientation responses, and prenatal cocaine exposure particularly tends to interfere with visual orientation.

State Control

State control in substance-exposed infants often is poorly organized, with the infants spending most of their time in states that shut them off from external stimulation. The infants frequently are very fragile,and their state changes tend to be abrupt and inappropriate with the child moving from sleeping to crying for no particular reason. Four most frequent patterns of state control problems in drug-exposed infants have been described:

In the first pattern, the infants pull down into a deep self-protective sleep in response to the first stimulation received. These infants remain asleep and in fact enter a deeper sleep as attempts to awaken them increase, indicating they are protecting themselves from what they perceive as negative stimulation.

The second pattern of state control demonstrated by drug-exposed infants is similar to the first except the infants cannot enter a sufficiently deep sleep to protect themselves from negative stimuli. They have difficulty blocking out negative stimuli, and rather than habituating or "getting use to," the stimuli, they remain asleep but continue to startle, whimper, change colors, breathe irregularly, and thrash around in response to stimulation.

The third pattern of state control problems for drug exposed infants is one in which they vacillate between sleeping and crying. With stimulation they break into agitated crying, and when the stimulation ceases they drop immediately back to a deep sleep. The continuous alternations between sleep and crying prevent the child from becoming sufficiently alert to respond adaptively to sound or to visual stimulation.

The final and most common pattern of state control for drug-exposed infants is similar to the third in that these infants use both sleeping and crying to shut themselves off from over-stimulation. However, these infants, when managed carefully, are able to reach brief periods of alertness and become responsive to the caretaker. The difficult aspect of this pattern is that the infants require intense but carefully regulated input. This generally requires a more sophisticated degree of parenting than most women with a history of drug abuse are capable of..

These neurobehavioral difficulties translate for the infant into problems of becoming easily overloaded and having difficulties in regulating behavior, characteristics that become important as we track the child through school age.

The Preschool-Age Child

Although we now have a growing body of research on the effects of perinatal substance abuse on the newborn, until relatively recently little attention has been paid to the long term implications of prenatal substance exposure. Drawing firm conclusions from many of these studies is difficult because it is hard to distinguish the purely biological effects of the prenatal exposure from the on-going environmental problems caused by living in a home with a substance-abusing parent.

The impact of alcohol on long-term infant growth and development has been examined by Streissguth, et al. (1989), who evaluated the effects of prenatal exposure to alcohol and/or tobacco on IQ scores at four years of age. They found a significant relationship between alcohol consumption during pregnancy and low IQ scores of the women's children at age four years.

Research is documenting the following long-term effects of prenatal substance exposure on children two to four years of age:

- *Tobacco smoking by the pregnant woman was related to poor language development and cognitive functioning in the three and four-year-old child (Fried and Watkinson, 1990).*

- *Alcohol exposure was related to decreased cognitive abilities at three years, and marijuana exposure was associated at four years with lower scores in the verbal and memory domains (Fried and Watkinson, 1990).*

- *Alcohol consumption during pregnancy by white, middle-class women had a negative effect on the IQ scores of their children at four years of age (Streissguth, et al, 1989).*

- *In a study of 30-month-old children prenatally exposed to cocaine, scores for cognitive development showed no differences between the cocaine-exposed and the control group infants (Hurt, et al, 1995).*

- *Prenatal exposure to cocaine and other drugs had minimal direct influence on cognitive development in a group of three year old children. The single most important predictor of cognitive development in this study was the home environment (Azuma and Chasnoff, 1993).*

- *A group of adopted, cocaine-exposed children showed significant delays on both expressive and verbal comprehension as compared with an unexposed matched control group of children (Nulman, et al, 1995).*

- *Developmental delays and behavioral problems demonstrated by a group of heroin exposed infants were found to be related to environmental deprivation and the fact that one or both parents in the home were addicted (Ornoy, et al, 1994).*

Fried and Watkinson examined the effects of prenatal exposure to marijuana, tobacco, and/or alcohol on developmental outcome of exposed children at 36 and 48 months of age. In their predominantly white, middle-class sample, the researchers found cigarette smoking to be related to poorer language development and cognitive functioning at both 36 and at 48 months of age. Alcohol exposure was related to decreased cognitive abilities at 36 months but not 48 months of age. Marijuana exposure was not related to cognitive abilities at 36 months but by 48 months was associated with lower scores in the verbal and memory areas.

Early data from the University of California at Los Angeles found that a group of 18 month-old children who had been exposed in-utero to cocaine had significantly lower developmental scores than a group of non-drug-exposed infants from similar family and socioeconomic backgrounds. However, it was noted that the mean developmental scores of the exposed group were still within the average range. The research- ers further indicated that the drug-exposed children showed striking deficits in the stability and organization of free play. They had less representational play than the control group. The majority of drug- exposed children demonstrated a high rate of scattering, batting, and picking up and putting down toys rather than sustained combining of toys, fantasy play, or curious exploration. This pattern of disruptive and disorganized play appears to be of a similar quality of neurobehavioral regulation as described in newborns affected by in- trauterine cocaine exposure.

These studies suggest drug-exposed children could be more likely to have developmental problems at the preschool level, which may continue into elementary school. Again, however, it should be remem- bered that the majority of these children continue to live in distressed environments, which also will have a negative effect on mastering de- velopmental skills.

The Early School-Age Child: The NAFARE Study

The team at the National Association for Families and Addiction Re- search and Education (NAFARE) has been funded by the U.S. Depart- ment of Education over the past ten years to conduct the only longitu- dinal, prospective study of school-age children prenatally exposed to cocaine and other drugs. The children enrolled in this study were born to women who were referred to the project during pregnancy before 15 weeks gestation from a general obstetric clinic, and the children have been followed continuously since birth.

Methods

The prenatally exposed children and the children recruited as a non- exposed control group are predominantly from a low socioeconomic class, with approximately 70% in both groups receiving public aid. The study subjects and the controls all lived in the central inner city of Chicago during pregnancy and early childhood and shared the same neighborhoods, schools, and general community environment. As might be expected, there has been some movement of the women and their children out of these areas into the larger metropolitan community over the past ten years.

At 4, 5, and 6 years of age, the outcomes of 170 children were evaluated. Ninety-five of these children had been born to women who used cocaine during pregnancy. Most of these women also had used additional nonopiate substances, including marijuana, alcohol, and/ or tobacco, in various combinations with the cocaine. The remaining 75 children had been born to women with no evidence of alcohol or illicit substance use, although ten smoked tobacco during pregnancy.

All the children were evaluated at NAFARE's research clinic, a comprehensive program of health care and developmental follow-up for substance-abusing women and their children. At the four-and five-year visits, measurements of weight, height, and head circumferences were collected by the pediatrician. Psychologists administered the Wechsler Primary and Preschool Scales of Intelligence-Revised (WPPSI-R) (Wechsler, 1989) which provides a global index of a child's level of cognitive ability (Full Scale IQ) and subscale scores on performance (Performance IQ) and verbal (Verbal IQ) capabilities. A research assistant administered the Structured Maternal Interview (SMI), an instrument created by the research team to evaluate maternal health, psychosocial status, and ongoing drug use patterns.

The Child Behavior Checklist (CBCL) (Achenbach, 1991) was completed by the mother or primary caretaker at each visit for each child at four, five, and six years. The CBCL is designed for parents and caretakers to record children's behavior in a standardized fashion. The CBCL provides eight descriptive behavioral patterns and two larger groupings of behaviors into "internalizing" and "externalizing" characteristics.

The mother or primary caretaker also completed the Home Screening Questionnaire (HSQ) at the four-year visit. The HSQ is a screening instrument completed by the caretaker that identifies factors within a young child's home environment related to the child's growth and development. It was designed to identify children at risk for developmental delay because of negative environmental influences. Total HSQ scores less than 41 are considered an indication of environmental risk (Coons, et al, 1981).

At six years of age, the children again underwent full physical evaluation. Cognitive functioning was evaluated utilizing the Wechsler Intelligence Scales for Children-III (WISC-III) (Wechsler, 1991), with Full Scale, Performance, and Verbal IQ's calculated. The mother or primary caretaker completed the CBCL and responded to the Structured Maternal Interview.

Results

The mothers in the two groups were of similar age, socioeconomic status, and racial distribution, and all lived in the same general neighborhoods. Average education level for both groups of mothers was eleventh grade. The drug-using women were heavy cocaine users with an average estimated frequency of cocaine use in the first trimester of pregnancy of 2.5 times per week with a range of .25 grams to 1 gram with each use. Forty percent of the women ceased all alcohol and illicit drug use by the beginning of the third trimester. However, in the period from time of delivery to follow up at the child's sixth birthday, all the drug-using women had relapsed to cocaine use at least once. At the six year assessment, 40 percent of the women who had used drugs during pregnancy were currently drug and alcohol free for an average of two years. The remaining 60 percent continued to use cocaine, alcohol, or some other illicit drug on an occasional to weekly basis. Among thecomparison group of women, although there was no use of alcohol or illicit drugs during pregnancy, five of the women had begun to use cocaine during the six years of follow up. The two groups of women showed similar levels of mild depression.

An important issue that became evident as we evaluated the lives of the children in the study was the high rate of exposure to violence. In the family histories of the women in both groups, there was a significant level of verbal and physical abuse. The children's exposure to violence varied significantly according to maternal history of substance use in pregnancy. Children in homes in which there was a history of substance abuse were much more likely to have lost a close relative to a violent death, to have been exposed to domestic violence within the home, and to have a mother who had been sexually abused or raped or who had previously physically abused a child.

Growth and Development

Both groups of children showed normal growth patterns through six years of age, although the children prenatally exposed to drugs had slightly smaller head size. The average IQ scores for both groups of children were at the lower end of the normal range, and there were no significant differences between the two groups at any age. However, the average IQ scores for both groups showed a steady decline over the three-year period, evidence of the negative effect of the impoverished environment in which they were all living. When evaluating this information, of course, the genetic influence of IQ also must be considered.

Mean Full Scale IQ Scores for Ages 3 to 6 years		
	Drug Exposed	Non-exposed
3 Years*	95	98
4 Years**	90	93
5 Years**	88	90
6 Years***	86	87

*   *Stanford-Binet*
** *WPPSI-R*
*** *WISC-III*

Behaviors

The primary caregivers' report on the behavior of their children prenatally exposed to cocaine and other drugs demonstrated significantly higher levels and rates of behavioral problems on all Child Behavior Checklist scales, as compared with nonexposed children. The scales that were most different between the two groups were the behaviors making up the "syndromes" of anxiety/depression, social problems, thought problems, attention problems, delinquent behavior, and aggressive behavior. Among the behaviors typical of each of these domains of behavior are:

- **anxiety/depression:** feels need to be perfect; feels unloved; feels others out to get him; feels worthless or inferior; nervous/highstrung/tense; sad/unhappy; worries; nervous/anxious

- **social problems**: acts too young for age; clingy; doesn't get along with others; gets teased a lot; not liked by other kids.

- **thought problems**: can't get mind off certain thoughts; repeats certain acts over and over; stares; strange ideas; strange behavior.

- **attention problems**: can't concentrate for long; can't sit still/restless; confused; daydreams; impulsive; poor schoolwork; stares.

- **delinquent behavior**: no guilt after misbehaving; lies/cheats; prefers older kids; steals; hangs around with kids who get into trouble.

- **aggressive behavior**: argues a lot; demands attention; destroys things of his own or others; disobedient at home and/or school; stubborn; sudden changes in mood; talks too much; unusually loud; temper tantrums/hot temper.

Mean Behavioral Scores at 4, 5, and 6 Years		
	Drug Exposed	Non-exposed
Anxiety/depression ***	3.70	2.03
Social **	2.53	1.79
Thought problems ***	1.18	0.46
Attention ***	4.17	2.54
Delinquent behaviors ***	2.65	1.47
Aggression ***	11.67	7.25
Internalizing *	6.71	4.74
Externalizing ***	14.32	8.72
Total problems ***	34.34	21.72

  * t test, p<.05
  ** t test, p<.01
  *** t test, p<.001

The first domain (anxiety/depression) is most typical of "internalizing" problems while the last two (delinquent behavior and aggressive behavior) are most typical of "externalizing" problems. Social problems, thought problems and attention problems do not clearly fall into either category, but may reflect difficulties in one of these other areas. For example, a child who is experiencing social difficulties may have problems with other children because of problems with anxiety and depression, or these same problems may reflect a child's aggressive behavior, making him disliked by others. These categories will be explained more fully below.

Internalizing Behaviors

Many behavioral problems have been classified into "internalizing" versus "externalizing." Internalizing behavioral patterns reflect those behaviors in which children expend much of their energy controlling feelings and inhibiting their own behavior, especially managing anger or other negative feelings toward others. We prefer the term "overcontrolled" to describe these children, as this better describes the energy expended in the service of these behaviors. Children with these problems typically show patterns of withdrawal, anxiety, social isolation, and depression. Drug-exposed children frequently show high levels of anxiety and are easily frustrated when presented with challenging situations, feel others are out to get them, and can feel unloved, worthless or inferior. The newborn infant who averted his gaze and withdrew into a deep sleep when overstimulated has become the little boy who wanders around the classroom without fully engaging in any activity, who gives up easily, or becomes upset when encountering any difficulty. These children are generally insecure and question their own capabilities, blaming themselves for their shortcomings.

Externalizing Behaviors

Behaviors often described as externalizing include those patterns of behavior that are disruptive to the classroom because of oppositionality and aggression. Traditionally, externalizing refers to patterns in which emotions are directed outward against others. However, these children often have other problems reflecting their difficulty controlling or inhibiting their behavior, such as impulsivity and overactivity. Thus we prefer the more descriptive term "undercontrolled." Prenatally exposed children exhibiting these patterns are often characterized as hyperactive, aggressive, and impulsive, which reflects their low threshold for stimulation and difficulty regulating themselves, especially when frustrated. The baby girl who could not easily move from a crying state to a calm interactive state can be seen as the preschooler who cannot calm down after recess or becomes out of control when she can't do what she wants.

Teacher reports of the children's behaviors, utilizing the Connors Behavioral Assessment, confirmed the mothers' reports, in that teachers described prenatally exposed children as exhibiting higher levels of anxiety and more hyperactivity. It should be noted that the teachers had no information regarding the children's possible prenatal drug exposure, so that factor did not influence their observations of the children. The picture of the drug exposed child that emerged from these two sources of behavioral evaluation was one in which the child is poorly organized, has trouble regulating his behavior, has trouble staying on track and completing a task, has higher activity levels, has low frustration levels and poor tolerance for stimulation (i.e., easily overstimulated), and experiences more anxiety and depression. These children also are reported to not respond to traditional behavioral interventions, especially those with negative connotations.

In evaluating the relationship of the child's multiple risk factors to his developmental and behavioral outcomes, it was found that prenatal exposure to drugs did not have an effect on the child's IQ at six years of age. However, if the mother continued to use drugs after pregnancy, the child's IQ scores were lower. This is an important point to make, for it emphasizes the need for schools to address family issues as well as the learning problems the child may demonstrate in the classroom. Surprisingly, the research data revealed that the quality of the home environment was not predictive of the behavioral problems exhibited by the prenatally exposed children, but that prenatal drug exposure directly predicted these behavioral problems.

In summary, the research data reveal that in this population of children prenatally exposed to cocaine and other drugs, prenatal exposure did not have a direct effect on the children's global intellectual functioning but that the home environment had a significant negative impact on cognitive development. However, prenatal exposure to cocaine and other drugs had a strong direct effect on the children's behavior at four to six years of age, with prenatally exposed children showing much higher rates and levels of behavioral problems with low thresholds for stimulation, a low tolerance for frustration, and difficulty with self-regulation.

The range and severity of behavioral difficulties is wide, and there simply is no way to identify the child in the classroom who was prenatally exposed to drugs. However, since our study indicates a significant relationship between prenatal drug exposure and behavior, we must be sure to view the exposed child as he or she should be viewed, not as willfully disobedient, but as a child whose neurological system may have been affected by the drugs that crossed the placenta during pregnancy.

Summary

Cocaine and other drugs had a strong direct effect on the children's behavior at four to six years of age, with prenatally exposed children showing much higher rates and levels of behavioral problems with low thresholds for stimulation, a low tolerance for frustration, and difficulty with self-regulation

Significance for the Schools

Information from this study raises a critical issue: the role of the family environment and school management in ameliorating the effects of prenatal substance exposure. Longitudinal research with other populations has shown that family functioning is a critical variable that predicts childhood behavioral outcome (Stanger, 1992). These studies have shown that family characteristics such as socioeconomic status, history of psychological problems, and number of adults in the household are significantly related to behavioral characteristics and school success in early and middle childhood. In addition, comprehensive school-based strategies must address the individual needs of the child as well as support the family in its attempt to provide a stable environment that enhances the child's growth and development.

Schools across the country are caught unprepared by the numbers of children and families needing special services because of prenatal drug exposure. And although there are many reports from schools all over the country describing substance-exposed children, most of them are misleading because of the difficulty of identifying the long standing psychosocial issues in the family, accurately identifying the pattern of intrauterine drug exposure, and, finally, accounting for the environment in which the child is being raised. Unfortunately, the following statement was recently published in a manual designed to meet the needs of drug-exposed children:

> "Research indicates that drug-exposed children differ from other children in intellectual functioning, quality of play, and security of attachment to their parents or parental figures. Their performance in school can be impaired by learning problems, attention deficit disorders, and language delays. Cocaine exposed children often have tantrums, poor impulse control, and an inability to regulate behavior." (Wilkes, 1993).

Two studies were cited for this information (Kronstadt, 1989; Davis, 1993). However, upon review, neither of them could substantiate these global claims of dysfunction. However, statements such as this have made schools leery and unnecessarily cautious about developing programs that support this high-risk group of children. These are the issues this manual can address because of its use of a well-described group of children, the prospective nature of the follow up, and the research-based intervention methods we are proposing.

Implications for Prevention

During the past decade, the federal government has supported a wide range of school based substance abuse prevention and treatment programs. In recent years there has also been increasing emphasis on the prevention and treatment of violent behavior. There is ample evidence that substance abuse and violence are interrelated and, most important, *that these behaviors are predictable*. Numerous researchers have found that psychological characteristics identified as early as age six can foretell drug use a decade later. A 1990 study by Jonathan Shedler and Jack Block of the University of California, Berkeley, defines such early characteristics as:

- the inability to get along well with other children or a lack of social competence;

- poor impulse control

- inattention and inability to concentrate; and

- a general sense of emotional distress or lability.

Noting that large-scale epidemiological studies have provided much-needed information about the prevalence and patterns of drug use, the demographics and certain psychosocial characteristics of drug users, Shedler and Block hold that these studies have been unable to provide the kind of in-depth, psychologically rich, clinically oriented information needed to inform effective intervention efforts. "By their very nature," the researchers conclude, "...current efforts at drug prevention are misguided to the extent that they focus on symptoms, rather than the psychological syndrome underlying drug abuse."

One of the most provocative aspects of the Shedler and Block research, from the perspective of school-based intervention strategies, is the role impaired parenting plays in fostering childhood behaviors that are characteristic of adolescent drug abusers. A longitudinal study initiated by Jeanne and Jack Block followed a group of San Francisco Bay area children from nursery school through age 18, performing carefully monitored and independently interpreted assessments at age 5, 7, 11, and 18. When the subjects were five years old, they each participated in joint assessment sessions with their mothers and in similar, but separate, sessions with their fathers. The purpose of the joint sessions was to allow observations of parent-child interactions under standard conditions. The children were given age-appropriate tasks and the parents were instructed to respond to their child's eventual difficulties with the tasks by providing whatever help they felt was needed.

The picture that emerged was indeed instructive. Those subjects who became frequent drug users by age 18 were deemed to have had poor maternal parenting. Observers of the mother-child interactions at age 5 perceived the mothers to be cold, critical, pressuring, and unresponsive to their children's needs. The fathers of frequent drug users were described by observers as "domineering," fathers who squelch spontaneity and creativity and who "...demand that things be done his way. He does not appear to enjoy being with his child and he ensures that his child does not enjoy being with him."

Children who grow up in families where alcohol or drug abuse is a factor are in a particularly high-risk group for developing problems with alcohol and other drug abuse and antisocial behavior. The U.S. Department of Health and Human Services estimated in 1993 that some 15.3 million adults in the United States suffer from alcohol abuse or dependence (West and Prinz, 1987) and up to 28 million children are thought to be growing up with at least one parent who is not only alcoholic but also may have problems with depression, antisocial behavior, and other psychological disturbances associated with impaired parenting (Davies, et al, 1989; Stoneman, et al, 1989). Such statistics suggest a substantial number of children in these homes are at risk for significant psychological impairment. In addition to heightened susceptibility for alcoholism in later life, the offspring of alcoholics frequently exhibit symptoms of hyperactivity, conduct disorder, oppositional behavior and delinquency during childhood and adolescence (Sher, et al, 1991; West and Prinz, 1988).

Thus, the predictability of adolescent drug abuse and antisocial (perhaps even violent) behavior is well documented in unrelated studies carried out over the past 10 years. This fact, coupled with the magnitude of the problem, suggests a multifaceted approach to early intervention, focused on the child and the family, is necessary. One such effort (Nye, Zucker, and Fitzgerald 1995), which used a school-based outreach protocol to contact and work with high-risk families, showed that family-based interventions had a preventive effect on later displays of both antisocial behavior and substance abuse by the child. These results are similar to the outcomes of other studies, all of which showed, however, that the degree of success in preventing future drug use and antisocial behavior was related to the level of involvement of the parents and ongoing family disruptors.

As one compares the outcome data from NAFARE's longitudinal study with the data from these diverse studies of the behavioral predictors of adolescent substance abuse, it is immediately evident that the behavioral characteristics of the children prenatally exposed to cocaine and other drugs and the high-risk characteristics for substance abuse are almost identical. It is clear that children prenatally exposed to drugs make up a very high-risk group of students who need the special attention of school-based intervention programs.

School-Based Intervention Strategies for Prenatally Exposed Children

Through this process of evaluating the long-term effects of prenatal drug exposure, analyzing the environmental factors that interact with the biological effects of the drugs, developing classroom intervention strategies that teachers can use to manage the behavioral difficulties of prenatally exposed children, and testing these strategies in schools across the country, several key findings were made:

1. *Intellectual functioning, as documented with standardized IQ tests, is too global a measure to define the educational prognosis for children prenatally exposed to alcohol and other drugs. While genetics probably have the single greatest impact on potential for cognitive development, the home environment is the critical mediator that most directly impedes or enhances the child's chances to ultimately fulfill that potential.*

2. *Children's learning and educational success is defined by multiple factors. Of these factors, the child's behavioral development is key.*

3. *Prenatally exposed children with undercontrolled behaviors (aggression, oppositionality, hyperactivity, short attention span, impulsivity) tend to act out in the classroom, especially when faced with developmentally demanding tasks, and disrupt the classroom. They quickly come to the attention of the teacher.*

4. *Prenatally exposed children with overcontrolled behaviors (fearfulness, crying, feeling unloved) are frequently overlooked by the teacher until it is discovered that the child is not following the presentation and discussion of the educational materials and is not making progress in the classroom. These children often are described by the teacher and the parent as "depressed;" however, they are more often exhibiting characteristics of anxiety and stress.*

6. *Children prenatally exposed to drugs require more direct and aggressive classroom interventions than children with behavioral problems who were not prenatally exposed. Some classic behavioral interventions, such as "time outs," are not successful and frequently result in escalation of the prenatally exposed child's behavior rather than helping him calm down. These children will require a wide range of individualized strategies to help them succeed.*

7. *A good classroom program will begin by empowering children to take control of their lives. For the long-term welfare of the child, he must be provided with the means to gain internal structuring capabilities. Rather than external control, internal empowerment combined with a strong external structure will provide the drug-exposed child the greatest possibility for success.*

8. *While there is no need for special settings and equipment, there is a critical need to integrate "best practices" for children who have been prenatally exposed to alcohol, cocaine, and other drugs into the school program.*

There are many misperceptions regarding children prenatally exposed to drugs. This book is an attempt to provide a research base to understanding this high-risk group of children. As stated in the plan developed to meet national education goals, "without a strong commitment and concerted effort on the part of every sector and every citizen to improve dramatically the performance of the nation's education system and each and every student, these goals will remain nothing more than a distant, unattainable vision." The National Association for Families and Addiction Research and Education hopes this book will help you in fulfilling your commitment to the children of this nation.

MANAGING BEHAVIOR EFFECTIVELY

Overview

The child who has been prenatally exposed to drugs may have behavioral problems that are directly related to his or her p r e natal and developmental history, current life circumstances, or a combination of several factors. Indeed, even after prenatal exposure and subsequent birth, many children live every day with substance abuse in their home environment where one or more parents or other family members use drugs. These circumstances can contribute further to behavioral and developmental problems that children demonstrate in the school setting.

Addicted parents' need for drugs or alcohol may take precedence over the needs of their children. Often drug-using parents are focused on "getting high," and the child can be a barrier to that goal. Such parents' interactions with their children tend to be erratic, as their drug use impacts their mood, resulting in frequent swings from impatient or angry to disinterested and apathetic. Such conditions create a world in which children's needs are not met, and the environment is generally unreliable and unpredictable. While nobody knows the exact toll of substance abuse on children, we do know that those who live in such home environments are at greater risk for violence, child abuse and becoming drug users themselves.

Moreover, teachers may not be aware that a student has been prenatally exposed but must respond to behaviors that could (or could not) be the result of exposure. While there are no "unique" interventions for behavioral problems associated with prenatal exposure, children with this history often do not respond to standard practices. Thus, we hope to provide an overarching template for understanding the special problems these students struggle with along with intervention strategies that have proved especially helpful for this population. Our goal is to help you assist children to manage themselves, rather than to ask you to control their behavior.

This section and the following one describe interventions that can be provided by the classroom teacher to effectively help students manage themselves so as to prevent, reduce, or eliminate the majority of behavioral problems. We start at the classroom level and move to individualized interventions that can be directed toward a specific child. At NAFARE, we assume that, for the most part, you as the classroom teacher are alone in the classroom with little or no immediate access to school psychologists or other behavioral specialists to assist you. Of course, there will be circumstances when specific children will present challenging behaviors that appear to be beyond your ability to remediate. These behaviors may be of such severity or a crisis nature that your best efforts may not be effective. In such cases, referral to other school personnel (social worker or psychologist) or outside professionals may be indicated.

Although referral to outside professionals may yield valuable diagnostic, intervention and consultation information, it may have limited value in the classroom. The child who is referred (and perhaps even hospitalized) will, in almost all cases, return to the classroom where you must manage behavior and help the child to learn. To be able to help the child when you have little or no assistance, you must have the tools necessary for understanding the problem so you can develop new management techniques. This book provides information that will help you to consider classroom and instructional factors that may be contributing to the behavioral problems and that, if changed, may reduce or eliminate the problem. If these adaptations do not work, then we provide you in Section Three with systematic help for developing effective individual interventions.

The Developmental Nature of Children's Behavior

To understand children's behavioral problems, it is important to have a perspective on behavior at different ages. In general, as children become older, their behavior becomes more focused and specific, with increasing self-control and responsibility. For instance, the mainly exploratory behavior of toddlers gradually gives way to behavior that is purposeful and organized, showing the beginning of industriousness and initiative by the time of school entry. A behavior that may be considered normal at one age can be a problem at another age. A good example is separation anxiety. In the first and second years of life, it is very normal for children to show anxiety and fear about being separated from their parents or primary caregivers. As children get older, this anxiety typically decreases to where the behavior occurs only in specific situations. For instance, many children become upset about leaving the parent on the first day of kindergarten. Normally, this anxiety subsides as the child becomes comfortable in the new surroundings. If the behavior continues throughout the primary grades, it is not normal and problems are indicated.

Trajectories

Development is often conceptualized as occurring along trajectories. A child's development occurs along multiple trajectories simultaneously, with each trajectory signifying a different domain or area of development, including cognitive, emotional, social, interpersonal, and motor. A child may be on a healthy trajectory in one or more domains but be on a less than optimal trajectory in another domain. These trajectories are assumed to be linear and continuous, unless something occurs to redirect the pathway. Thus, the goal for those of us who work with children is to affect the trajectory in a positive way, so that the less optimal pathways are impeded and the long-term trajectory of a given child is modified in the normal and healthy direction. Many conditions contribute to developmental vulnerability along one or more pathways.

Just Being a Kid

When behavioral problems occur in the classroom, there may be a tendency to forget that, at times, the child is "just being a kid." The teacher should not assume every inappropriate behavior or series of behaviors indicates the presence of a problem. Often, even the child who has been identified as having behavioral problems simply may be exhibiting behavior typical of other children of the same age. There are several behaviors that all children may show at different times, depending on the circumstances and the child's characteristics. Some of these behaviors include lack of attention, distractibility, withdrawal, aggressiveness, mild disobedience, and being off task.

Beyond "Normal": When Behaviors Become Problems

Teachers and parents often ask how to know when a behavior is "abnormal" or problematic versus when it is merely a manifestation of a wide range of "normal." Among the criteria for making this determination are: frequency of the behavior, duration of the problem, whether the behavior is having a detrimental impact on the child's learning, and whether the child's relationships with peers or adults are negatively affected.

Frequency

"Frequency" refers to how often a behavior occurs and whether it occurs frequently enough to impact a child's success in one of the domains of development. Examples include failure to complete assignments, number of times a student engages in off-task behavior, or the frequency of the child's talking without permission. An important question to ask is, "Do such behaviors occur with such frequency that they interfere with healthy learning or relationships?"

Duration

How long a behavior persists is referred to as duration. If an undesired or inappropriate behavior persists for so long that the child's performance is affected, then the behavior becomes problematic. Examples include how long a child remains off task or how pervasively a child withdraws from social situations.

In most cases, assessing both frequency and duration is an important first step in determining if there is a deleterious effect on the child's successful development. For example, the child may be off task for several minutes at a time (duration), while making distracting noises or getting out of his chair several times during the same period (frequency). It may be necessary to consider both the time off task as well as the frequency of other negative behaviors that occur during that time. However, the most important consideration is whether the behavior is having an adverse impact on the child's learning, social relationships with peers, and interactions with adults.

Types of Children's Behavioral Problems

When teachers and parents observe children's behavioral problems, there may be a pattern, such as aggressiveness, withdrawal, unhappiness, or anxiety. Many times, the behaviors do not appear to have a pattern or to be caused by identifiable events. For example, a child may suddenly become aggressive for no apparent reason, causing confusion and uncertainty as to how to intervene. Having a systematic understanding of children's behavioral problems is the first step in developing effective interventions in the classroom and for individual children.

Overcontrolled behavior

Overcontrolled behavior refers to those patterns in which children expend much energy controlling their feelings and inhibiting their behavior. These children often show patterns of withdrawal and social isolation and may be difficult to identify because they usually are not disruptive. They often sit in the back of the classroom and are perceived as being shy, compliant and reluctant to engage in activities. Up to ten percent of all children have these kinds of problems, but they are identified in fewer than half the cases.

Overcontrolled behaviors are sometimes also referred to as "internalizing patterns." The child's feelings are directed inwardly or "internally" so that the child experiences depression, anxiety or low self-esteem and lacks self-confidence and self-efficacy. The classroom teacher should be alert to indications of these patterns, as children who have been exposed to alcohol, cocaine and other drugs and who live in stressful environments are more likely to demonstrate them.

NAFARE's population of substance-exposed children commonly exhibit the following behavioral patterns which fall under the overcontrolled category:

- feelings of worthlessness

- secretiveness

- worry

- lack of communication

- sadness

- complaints of being unloved

- belief that others are out to get him/her

- fearfulness

- staring

- withdrawal

- sulking

- peer difficulties

- need to be perfect.

■ Scenario-Susie - excessive talking

Susie is talking in class without permission, and the teacher repri-
mands her. Susie becomes very quiet for the next hour. However,
observing her on the playground during recess, she interacts well and
shows no signs of withdrawal. Back in the classroom, she behaves
appropriately and responds well to directions and completes tasks.

Response to Scenario-Susie

Since past observations of Susie's behavior suggest that usually she is
well-behaved, her brief withdrawal behavior in response to the reprimand is situation-specific and should not be considered an internalizing pattern. Almost all children, at times, will show the talking behavior
of Susie (i.e., "just being a kid") so it is not a serious problem that
warrants specific interventions.

Compare this scenario to Sammy.

■ Scenario-Sammy

Sammy does not seem to enjoy working with other children, but rather
spends much of his time alone, both in and out of the classroom, and
rarely smiles. He has a need for everything to be perfect, and lack of
perfection seems to confirm beliefs of his inadequacy. He rarely par-
ticipates in classroom activities or volunteers answers, and he seems
very tense and uncomfortable when called upon to participate, often
lowering his eyes and not responding. When he does respond he fre-
quently speaks so softly he cannot be heard.

Response to Scenario - Sammy

Although much more information would be needed in an actual case, the withdrawal shown here is part of a chronic pattern that is presumed to be interfering with Sammy's schoolwork. Drug exposed children have a low tolerance for frustration and often attempt to withdraw from typical classroom situations. Their behavior is often prompted by fear and insecurity. Children who live in environments in which drugs are being used often do not have effective conversational skills because their parents have failed to respond positively to their verbal initiations, resulting in a lack of experience with verbal interaction and expression. Such children's social anxiety can be a result of their repeated mistreatment or abuse at home. Often they lapse into daydreaming as an escape from anxieties. If the teacher suspects this is the case, referral may be indicated and collaboration with other professionals may be needed as well. However, the teacher will be the primary person in a position to help the child with these difficult feelings and to develop strategies to improve his classroom functioning.

The essential difference between Susie and Sammy is Susie's behavior is in direct response to a specific situation and is not a chronic pattern, while Sammy has exhibited a long-term pattern of dysfunction that seems to bridge different situations and conditions.

Undercontrolled Behavior

Undercontrolled behavior patterns are more easily identified in children because the behaviors tend to be disruptive. "Acting out" is one way that these types of behaviors often are labeled. Whereas children with overcontrolled or internalizing behavior tend to inhibit behavior, turning their feelings inward, the undercontrolled (also termed "externalizing") child has much difficulty in inhibiting or controlling behavior and expresses his feelings outwardly, usually against others.

There are two categories of behaviors that fall under the larger grouping of undercontrolled. Children who have diagnoses of conduct disorder and oppositional-defiant disorder are one type because they have difficulty managing aggression and anger. Another category is children who meet criteria for attention deficit disorder or attention deficit hyperactivity disorder. These children have difficulty with sustained attention to task and are distractible and impulsive. Sometimes they are overactive or "hyper." Their difficulty with self-management may or may not include problems with aggression.

Specific undercontrolled behaviors include:

Aggressive Type	ADD/ADHD
• defiance or oppositionality	• inability to sit still/overactiveness
• aggressiveness/fighting	• failure to complete tasks
• refusal to follow directions	• difficulty following directions
• disrupting class, temper tantrums	• inattentiveness
• impulsivity	• mpulsivity
• destructiveness	• stealing
• stealing	

While some children fit behaviors listed in both categories, many fit only one or the other. It is important to distinguish those who have difficulty with attention and distractibility but are able to control and manage aggression and anger, and vice versa. The strategies for these different behavioral patterns are distinct, and thus assessment of the actual behaviors needs to be carefully delineated.

Children who show these types of behaviors are likely to make classroom management more difficult. They often reduce instructional time as the teacher attempts to curb the behaviors.

■ Scenario-Enrico (agressive, oppositional)

Enrico has a history of becoming aggressive and defiant when given directions and sometimes openly refuses to do as he is asked, directing considerable hostility toward the teacher. If he is teased by another student, Enrico becomes very angry and often responds with aggression, including hitting or kicking. Often these incidents occur at recess or on the bus. Although this behavior does not occur every day, it happens with enough frequency (a few times per week) and is sufficiently disruptive that the teacher cannot ignore it. Enrico has few friends and hangs out with other students who have a tendency to get into trouble with teachers and administrators for similar behavior.

Response to Scenario - Enrico

Enrico is demonstrating undercontrolled or externalized aggressive behavior that is a problem in the classroom and also consigns him to a peer group that serves to reinforce his behavior. For many oppositional children, defiance to authority is an effort to maintain a sense of personal control in situations that make them feel vulnerable. Often this reflects negative experiences with parents who have not provided their child with enough sense of control or have responded punitively to autonomy seeking. These children also have difficulty sharing with other children, as they feel the need to control the situation to avoid the feeling of vulnerability that comes with shared control. Such children, because of underlying insecurity, are also very sensitive to name calling and other small slights.

■ Scenario-Andrea (distractible, impulsive)

Andrea tends to be very distractible in class, so that when multiple activities are occurring at one time, or someone walks into the room, she loses track of what she is doing. This often results in incomplete tasks. In addition, she is quite impulsive, resulting in several of her answers on written materials being incorrect, even though she knows the right answer when given one-on-one help. When given assignments, she often completes only about half before she gets lost or disorganized. She has few friends because they tire of her apparent immaturity and constant disruptiveness.

Response to Scenario - Andrea

Andrea is showing undercontrolled behaviors typical of ADD/ADHD patterns. She is disruptive in the classroom because she has difficulties managing her behavior sufficiently to function academically and socially. Children who are prenatally drug-exposed often show similar patterns of behavior. ADD/ADHD experts believe these problems are a result of a biochemical disorder of the brain that is largely hereditary. Our research indicates that prenatal drug exposure may affect neurotransmitter fuctioning, which prevents the brain from functioning in a predictable, organized way. While the causes of ADD/ADHD and behavioral difficulties due to prenatal drug exposure probably are different, the results appear to be quite similar.

Mixed Behaviors

Often children do not show only one type of behavior but show signs of both types of behaviors. We refer to these patterns as "mixed," i.e., those that are not clearly of only the undercontrolled or overcontrolled type. However, undercontrolled behavior patterns may overshadow overcontrolled patterns because they are, by definition, disruptive in nature. Therefore, it should not be assumed that internalizing problems are not present just because a child displays only undercontrolled patterns. For the teacher, it is important to try to determine what behavioral patterns are most characteristic of the child and then begin to develop an intervention. The interventions described in this book are based, in part, upon this concept of undercontrolled and overcontolled and will be discussed in more detail later.

■ Scenario-Bobby (withdrawal, social isolation)

Bobby is a quiet and shy seven-year-old boy who has very few friends. He does not have nice clothes and is unkempt, and many of his peers tease him and call him names. When the class is divided into groups to work on a project, members of Bobby's group have been heard making unkind remarks loud enough for everyone to hear. At times, Bobby is provoked and becomes aggressive toward others. Usually, the behavior is brief, but it does add to his difficulties.

Response to Scenario - Bobby

In this situation, Bobby shows both undercontrolled and overcontrolled problems, although withdrawal and social isolation may be the primary cause of his overcontrolled behavior. Most of the literature suggests the best solution for peer rejection problems is to establish the classroom as a learning community that features a "we" feeling and positive group identity. In classrooms where prosocial values such as self-control, self-discipline, and the need to care for oneself and for one another are taught, the frequency of peer rejection problems is minimized. Teaching simple, clear values is especially important for children in drug-abusing families, since they are often victims of social and emotional isolation. Such families seldom offer adaptive alternatives to inappropriate behavior, so the child does not know how to respond in social situations. Programs such as those described by Ruth Sidney Charney

(1992) are especially useful in establishing a responsive classroom environment.

Children who were prenatally exposed to drugs often exhibit mixed pictures. They often have difficulty managing their anger in addition to problems with distractibility and impulsivity. However, these children also frequently experience high levels of anxiety and feel depressed.

Other types of behavioral problems do not fit easily into this categorization of overcontrolled and undercontrolled. These include thought problems, such as obsessive-compulsive problems or disorientation, and some types of social problems, e.g., the child seeks peer friendships but is ignored or not accepted even if he does not exhibit overly aggressive or withdrawn patterns. Lack of social skills can lead to a range of difficulties.

Before we continue through the next part of Section Two, let's pause for a moment to check our understanding of the concepts introduced so far.

 *Thinking About It*

We have prepared some examples of the types of behaviors discussed above. As you read the examples think about how you would categorize each child. A discussion of each case follows. (Categories to include: Undercontrolled - Aggression; Undercontrolled - Attention; Overcontrolled; Mixed; Social problems)

■ Case Study - Nilda (distractability)

Nilda never seems to finish an assignment. She cannot stay in her seat. She is constantly getting up to go out to the hall or to the window to see what is going on. She almost never gets back on task after a distraction.

Discussion

This is an example of undercontrolled-attention behavior. Nilda is easily distracted, is unable to sit still and fails to complete tasks. While these behaviors are characteristic of children with ADD, they also are frequently associated with substance-exposed children. Braswell and

Bloomquist (1991) have found that teaching children to self-monitor their behavior and productivity has been very successful because many children with such deficits are not aware of the frequency of their tuning out. However, interventions for primary-age children should be more environmental, since they generally are not developmentally ready to benefit from direct cognitive interventions. Interventions such as study carrels, frequent teacher monitoring and intervention, headphones to play white noise or soft music to block out distractions, seating distractible students away from hallways and windows, or other types of strategies that reduce distractions are all beneficial to children who are easily drawn off task.

■ Case Study - Lucy (Controlling)

Lucy has outbursts of anger when her requests are not immediately met. When reprimanded she becomes sullen or pouts or tries to lay blame on someone else. She asks for help, but when the teacher tries to explain the assignment she hums, stares out the window and taps her pencil on the desk. In group situations she is very controlling. If she cannot be the "leader" all the time she refuse to participate and withdraws from the group. She is always the last to get in line and often pretends not to hear instructions even when they are directed specifically at her.

Discussion

Lucy's behavior is referred to as "mixed" because her behavior is not clearly undercontrolled or overcontrolled. Children rarely show only one type of behavior and may show many signs of both types. The child of an addicted parent lives in a home environment that is inconsistent or in constant conflict. These parents create a world that is often unreliable and upredictable. Children in this type of home feel confused as to how to please their parents and how to respond to social situations appropriately. Often such children try to establish a sense of control over their lives by resisting external controls. Generally, techniques that encourage children to express their feelings directly will help them develop more positive communication skills. By adjusting the curriculum and instruction to allow more choice options, teachers can develop the child's need to feel she can have a role in deciding what she does. Thus she can start to have a sense of control over her life.

■ **Case Study - Martin (agressive)**

Martin is working at his desk. Another child accidentally brushes by Martin's desk causing Martin's papers to fall on the floor. Martin jumps out of his seat and pushes the child to the ground. Martin also displays this behavior frequently on the playground and during group work.

Discussion

Martin's reaction represents characteristics of undercontrolled behavior, aggressiveness, and impulsivity. Recent literature indicates that hostile agressive behavior is often a result of modeling by parents (Brophy 1996). Our studies have shown substance-exposed children to be at high risk for exposure to violence. Parents are often hostile and abusive to each other and frequently use excessive physical punishment as a means of discipline. Thus, rather than teaching skills of conflict resolution, how to define and verbalize feelings, social problem solving, and self-management, drug-abusing parents often teach their children by example that "a good offense is the best defense." Such children often respond to even small slights as if they were threats to their safety. In addition, if the child is drug-exposed, there is greater likelihood of overall impulsivity and a low threshold for frustration, both of which contribute further to the kind of response Martin displays.

■ **Case Study - Brian (withdrawn)**

Brian is a very quiet first-grader who spends most of his time alone. He does not join in any group activities and stands on the edge of the playground watching other children play. In the classroom he quietly sits at his desk, often sucking his thumb and gazing into space. He has never brought in items for show-and-tell and does not volunteer any answers or participate in class discussions.

Discussion

Brian is an example of an internalized-withdrawn child who is likely quite shy. He appears to be unhappy and detached. He is withdrawn from others and has very few friends. Children like Brian are often not identified because they are compliant and cooperative in the classroom. Substance-exposed children often withdraw or lapse into daydreaming as an attempt to escape from their anxieties. They often have a poor self-image and negative expectations of themselves and others as a result of failure or mistreatment.

■ Case Study - Yolanda (defeatist)

Yolanda is of average ability but appears to make very little effort to do her assignments. She complains that assignments are too hard before even attempting them. When the teacher gives her individual attention she finds Yolanda is very capable of doing the work assigned. Yolanda gets frustrated and disgusted very easily; instead of trying to solve a problem she gives up, convincing herself she cannot handle it and saying she is "stupid."

Discussion

Yolanda tends to internalize her feelings of anger and helplessness and thus sets up a pattern of failure that serves to reconfirm her beliefs. She has a low self-image and is defeated before she starts. When she begins a task she applies very little effort and gives up as soon as she encounters any difficulty. Yolanda's behavior is typical of the low frustration tolerance and organizational difficulties exhibited in children who have been substance-exposed.

Behavior Problems and the Prenatally-Exposed Child

Research Findings

NAFARE has been following a sample of children over the past several years and has assessed their behavior as perceived by parents and teachers. As stated in Section One, we have found a relationship between prenatal drug exposure and behavioral problems in this group of children. However, as in the previous discussion, many of these children also come from stressful and unstable environments that can have significant effects on behavior, attention, and achievement. It is difficult, if not impossible, to distinguish causal factors as they dynamically interact with each other. However, the classroom teacher, who may not know the child has been prenatally exposed, must nevertheless attempt to deal with the resulting behavior and learning problems.

In the research conducted by NAFARE, using the undercontrolled/overcontrolled model, certain behaviors are reported more frequently in children prenatally exposed to alcohol, cocaine, and other drugs. These include:

- Overcontrolled: withdrawal, feelings of worthlessness, secretiveness, staring, excessive worry, refusal to talk, sadness, complaints of being unloved, belief that others are out to get him/her, need to be perfect.

- Undercontrolled-aggressive: defiant/oppositional, disobedient, temper problems, aggressiveness, impulsivity, destructiveness.

- Undercontrolled-attention problems: poor sustained attention, impulsivity, distractibility, restlessness/moving, incomplete work, difficulty following directions and working independently

- Mixed: pouting/sulking, bothering others, daydreaming, insecurity, lack of self-efficacy.

Children usually exhibit behaviors that fit more than one category, although problems tend to cluster in one or two groups. Often it is the combination of behaviors that are challenging in the classroom setting. Intervening in these types of behavioral difficulties that reflect both biological and environmental factors is often difficult. Traditional behavior modification approaches, which stress reinforcement of good behavior and use time out and cost response approaches to withhold reinforcement generally have been found ineffective when used with the drug-exposed children in our study. The children's self-regulatory difficulties, lack of ability to organize themselves, and increased anxiety levels lead them to respond to the negative and punitive nature of these interventions with heightened behavior. Since interventions such as time out and cost response increase tension and anxiety in the child, the behavior that one wants to reduce is paradoxically escalated, and the child continues to discharge his tension through the very behaviors the teacher is seeking to reduce. In our research, implementing preventive strategies that emphasize helping children learn to regulate themselves and providing positive incentives to help them exert the special effort needed have been far more effective in working with drug- exposed children who exhibit undercontrolled behavior.

Sources of Child Behavioral Problems

It is common for parents and teachers to ask why children exhibit behavioral and emotional difficulties, expecting that knowing the causes will help them to develop methods to deal with the problems. It also is common for adults to assume the problems are the product of some inherent characteristics of the child or of a dysfunctional family situation. However, viewing the child as the sole or primary source of behavioral problems is inappropriate. Therefore, we should consider multiple sources of influence: ecological factors, developmental or child-specific characteristics, and interactions between these two sources.

Ecological factors

Ecological factors are the characteristics of a child's home, family relationships, neighborhood and school climate that influence a child's development and well-being (Bronfenbrenner 1979). It is important to remember that each child is embedded within many layers of ecology, and that the influences may be indirect. For example, not only are children affected by the behavior of their parents, but their parents, in turn, are affected by the neighborhood environment, economic stressors, and other environmental conditions. The larger school environment in which a classroom is embedded similarly affects the child directly, but also affects the child through how that larger environment affects the teacher and other school personnel who work with the child. Children always bring the influence of the larger ecologies in which they are embedded to the classroom in ways that contribute to behavior, learning and relationship problems.

Home and family relationships

Ineffective parenting, such as lack of parenting skills, difficulty setting limits or use of inappropriate punishment, can affect a child's behavior in the classroom as well as her response to authority. If parents are using drugs, the home environment likely is unpredictable and lacks structure. In addition, drug-using parents are usually struggling to manage the larger ecological conditions associated with poverty, including many children in the home, unsafe neighborhoods, violence, lack of community resources, including poor medical care and few recreational opportunities, and concerns about meeting the family's basic needs. All these conditions can contribute to childhood problems. These factors can have considerable implications for the teacher, especially when he or she attempts to develop a home-school partnership or to enlist the parents' aid in addressing behavioral problems.

Classroom Factors

Situational factors in the home, such as pending divorce or foster placement, can contribute to the presence of behavioral problems. Children in these situations often struggle to deal with the stress associated with their circumstances, which often makes them feel they have no control. Coping with and adapting to stress and situational difficulties may result in a variety of inappropriate behaviors, which may not be recognized by an adult as the child's adaptive strategies. However, even when behaviors are related to situational factors, they often can be reduced by effective management procedures.

When addressing classroom behavioral and learning problems, you should consider that these difficulties may arise from several sources, both in and out of the classroom. While you may not be able to change all the contributing ecological factors, you do have direct control of the ecological characteristics of your classroom. You will also have to deal with the larger school ecology and its impact on you and the students. Is your school experienced as a safe place? Do children feel important and respected? Are parents welcome in the school? Is the school facility clean and attractive? Does the environment feel impoverished or full of resources? Assessing the impact of the school climate on yourself as well as on your students can help you understand the larger situation affecting your students. So, while it is easy to identify the child's family situation as the problem, you may have little opportunity to change it directly. Your efforts to engage the parents as helpers may or may not be successful. Therefore, you should focus on what you can do to help children develop better behavioral control through effective classroom management and in helping them manage the larger school environment.

Although it is common for adults to attribute the sources of behavioral problems to the child and home, there is ample research evidence, as well as classroom experience, to indicate classroom ecological factors contribute significantly to behavioral problems. Consideration of the classroom environment thus is critical for the successful management of behavioral problems in the classroom. It also is much easier to change current circumstances that contribute to a problem than it is to change a child's characteristics. For example, if a child has an attention problem that is intensified in a situation where he is easily distracted, it will be much more effective to change the distracting situation than attempt to train the child to be more attentive. Although the child still may have the attention problem, it will be manifested to a much lesser extent if the situation can be changed.

Many types of classroom situational factors can influence a child's behavior and can become the focus for intervention in the classroom:

- Large class sizes or grouping problems

- Structure or arrangement of the classroom

- Unclear or inappropriate expectations for behavior

- Tasks or instructional conditions that are inappropriate for the child

- Presence of several children who present management difficulties

- Lack of administrative and instructional support for the teacher.

It is instructive to examine one of these situational factors that may contribute to a child's behavior - unrealistic expectations from adults. If a child is expected to do more than he can do, he may become frustrated, and no amount of coaxing, coercion, or management techniques will enable him to do something he cannot do. A child may react regatively to the pressure by showing behavior such as refusal to cooperate, disruptiveness, inattentiveness, or inconsistent performance. If adults are not aware a child is being asked to do something beyond her current skill level, such behavior is assumed to be willful disobedience. Often a change in expectations may solve the problem.

Although asking a child to do something beyond her ability may cause frustration, so can asking her to do less than she is capable of. When adults have lower expectations of what the child can do, it can lead to boredom and loss of interest in tasks, which may also result in misbehavior. For example, a child, Ken, seen recently in our research program, is ten years old and in the fourth grade in an inner-city public school. He lives in a foster home where he was placed when he was five. When evaluated, Ken worked efficently and accurately, with reading and spelling skills at eighth-grade level and math skills at fifth-grade level. However, there were many complaints about his behavior, both from his foster mother and from the school. How could this be? A child learning so efficiently yet acting disruptively and being disparaged by adults suggests some misunderstanding.

As this discrepancy was discussed with the school, it became clear that Ken finishes his work long before his peers and is not given additional challenging and structured work assignments. Bored, Ken begins to disturb other children, gets out of his seat, and otherwise becomes distruptive. Similarly, at home, inadequate structure and challenge in activities and relationships is replaced by Ken challenging the adults in his life; thus, he is considered "difficult."

Child-Specific Factors

Child-specific factors include a broad range of factors that increase a child's vulnerability to developing behavioral problems and often are enhanced by home and family difficulties:

(1) neurological/biological

(2) developmental problems

(3) emotional factors

(4) motivational factors.

Neurological/Biological Factors

Biological factors are present when a child has a history of a medical or physical problem that has accompanying behavioral manifestations, such as attention difficulties, impulsivity, or low tolerance for frustration. Our research has confirmed a direct relationship between behavior and the impact of prenatal substance exposure. We believe that during the course of pregnancy drugs crossing the placenta directly affect the brain at the level of the neurotransmitters, interfering with the ability to function in a predictable, organized way. Children who are substance-exposed have difficulty regulating their behavior, reaching a level of overstimulation easily. Once that threshold is reached, they often are unable to regain control of their behavior.

There may be a tendency by some to assume that if behavioral problems have a neurological or biological basis, little can be done other than to try to control them using medication or through external behavioral control. There is ample research evidence and actual experience to indicate that behavioral problems can be greatly reduced or managed successfully to the point that a child can perform well in the classroom. For example, children with attention deficit problems have been taught methods that significantly improve their attention. Additionally, our clinical and field testing experience indicates many of the problems experienced by substance-exposed children can be significantly improved by a change in the teacher's attitude. This change may be brought about through increased understanding of the difficulties that substance-exposed children have in managing frustration and stimulation and in regulating and organizing themselves.

Developmental Problems

Developmental problems or delays, which may or may not have an identifiable neurological or biological basis, may also be a source of behavioral problems. Developmental disorders such as an expressive language disorder often lead to social withdrawal, heightened frustration resulting in tantrums or outbursts, and academic difficulties. Other developmental disorders, such as autism, are diagnosed because of the existence of disruptive or unusual behaviors and social interaction. As with neurologically or biologically based behavioral problems, behaviors that reflect developmental delays or disorders can be influenced by how the teacher handles them. Further, many of these behaviors can be effectively addressed with the management techniques that reflect an understanding of the underlying problem.

Health Factors

Clearly, it is important to make certain that children living in drug-affected environments are properly screened for health problems and developmental delays. Whether due to parental ignorance or neglect or lack of adequate available services, children's poor health or delayed development can have great influence on their ability to thrive in the classroom environment. Early health and developmental screenings can be critical in ensuring that each child has the opportunity to reach her full potential.

Emotional Factors

A child's emotional problems, such as anxiety, depression, anger, and hostility, can be a source of classroom problems. Many times, the causes of these problems are not clear, although they often reflect other domains of problems, such as ecological issues. Drug-exposed children are even more vulnerable to the toll of emotional stressors because they have difficulty with the increased tension such stressors create. They quickly get disorganized but do not understand their loss of control and are confused and frightened by it. Such children are frequently identified as "willfully disobedient" or "behavior problems" by the teacher who, by misunderstanding the nature of the child's problem, causes increased anxiety and stress in the child. It is not uncommon for drug-exposed children to develop emotional problems as a result of being misunderstood by their teachers or parents. Emotional problems often factor into disruptive classroom behaviors, although other children with emotional problems can be easily overlooked because they are underreactive, withdrawn or quiet.

Motivational Factors

Motivational factors are important contributors to children's classroom behaviors. When children show behavioral problems, they often are looking for a particular outcome. Researchers have identified seven outcomes children may seek when they show dysfunctional behavior.

Behavior	Motivation
Seeks control of events and situations	Power/Control
Seeks to avoid a task or escape a consequence or negative situation, seeks to avoid threatening situations or feelings of vulnerability	Protection/Escape/Avoidance
Tries to set self apart from others, seeks to be the focus (seeking recognition, affirmation)	Attention
Seeks to relate to others	Acceptance/Affiliation
Seeks forum for expression of needs, skills, or talents	Self-expression
Seeks reward or enjoyment at own direction	Gratification
Seeks settlement of differences or to "get even"	Justice/Revenge

These motivational factors often are major contributors to child behavioral problems. If they are present and the teacher can identify them, it may be possible to make adjustments in the classroom that will improve the child's behavior. While behavioral problems may reflect such motivational goals, remember that for some children behavior may reflect the child's effort to cope with neurological/biological or developmental vulnerabilities. When a child is behaving negatively, it is often more productive for the teacher to try to determine what the child hopes to achieve with the misbehavior rather than engage in punitive measures. If a reason can be found, then it is possible to develop interventions that can successfully address it.

Interactions between child-specific and ecological factors

Interactions between ecological factors and child-specific sources can create particular problems for the teacher. Let us assume a child has a tendency to be hyperactive and inattentive (child-specific factors), and comes from a home in which the parents are using drugs and not providing adequate structure and limit-setting for their child (ecological factors), and that the child lives in a neighborhood with few resources and considerable danger. While the child may show some of the distractibility and impulsivity that are characteristic of a child with attention deficit problems, it is likely the ecology of the home and neighborhood, including lack of structure and routine, inconsistent discipline, exposure to violence and danger, and few positive role models, further exacerbates these behavioral tendencies and makes the problems worse. Further, the parents initially may not be in a position to be a helpful resource as you, the teacher, attempt to deal with the behaviors in the classroom.

Another common scenario that reflects this interaction of ecological and child-specific factors regards child abuse. Often the child who is difficult to manage because of poor behavioral control is the target of abuse because of the parent's lack of parenting skills and poor self-control. Overly punitive physical punishment, being secluded for long periods of time, or being emotionally abused by cruel words and lack of love all can contribute further to a child's behavioral problems. Abused children often exhibit a range of behavior problems that include both undercontrolled and overcontrolled patterns. In addition, they often do not trust adult authorities, further contributing to patterns of oppositionality and defiance. All these issues come together and interfere with the learning process and concentration.

Children's Misbehavior as Messages

It is common for adults to react to children's misbehavior by seeking to control, change, or eliminate it. At NAFARE, we believe it is useful to consider misbehavior as a message that something is wrong that the child does not know how to correct. Usually the behavior is functional in some way — that is, it is serving in the capacity of helping a child cope with anxiety, anger, frustration, overstimulation or other experience. Because the behavior you want to eliminate is functional, you will be unsuccessful in your efforts unless you help the child find alternative behaviors that are more appropriate or adaptive.

Behavior Messages

The messages of behavior are not always easy to understand, and very different behaviors may reflect the same message. Sometimes, there may be multiple messages. Suppose Samantha tends to have trouble academically and becomes disruptive during independent seatwork. She could be sending one of multiple messages, such as "I can't do this because it's too hard," "I need some help," "I can't structure my work by myself," "I'm frustrated," "I just came back from recess and can't settle down to do my work," or "I'm angry with Mrs. Smith for giving me something so hard to do." Following are some behaviors that may occur and some possible messages being sent.

Behaviors	Message
Withdrawal	"I'm scared." "No one likes me." "I'm sad." "I don't know how to reach out to others."
Shyness	"I'm overwhelmed." "I'm unsure of myself." "I can't cope with this."
Submissiveness	"I don't feel good about myself." "I don't know what to do."
Aggressiveness	"I can't do this, it's too hard." "I'm not being treated fairly." "I'm frustrated." "I'm angry." "I can't cope with this."
Inattention	"I'm bored." "I don't know what to do." "I need a break." "I got distracted."
Refusal to comply	"I'm mad and I don't want to be here." "This is not fair." "If I try, I'll fail."
Non-completion of tasks	"I don't know how to do this." "This is too hard." "I don't know how to organize this." "I got distracted and forgot what I was doing."

There are many other messages children can send through their behavior, and it may be difficult to determine what they are trying to communicate. Usually, however, through experience with that child, the teacher can read the message, figure out the function of the behavior and take some action. The important thing to remember is that a message is there, and if you can figure it out, you may well be on your way to solving the problem quickly.

Teacher Empathy and Empowerment

The most important aspect of reading and responding to messages is the basic but critical ability to be empathic. This means successfully picking up on the message embedded in behaviors, and responding empathically to that message and the function it is serving. Empathic, reflective statements such as, "I see that you're angry about this," or "It seems like you're having trouble organizing this work by yourself," or "I know it was easy to be distracted by the principal's announcement, but now let's see if we can focus on the work and remember what we need to do," can be very powerful interventions in and of themselves, as they allow a child to feel understood, enhancing his sense of trust and safety with that adult.

However, in the everyday world of the classroom, the teacher often reaches the point where she feels unable to deal with the problems facing her. It is hard to feel empathy when you feel powerless. So the teacher responds out of her own frustration. Empowerment is the degree to which the teacher feels capable of dealing with classroom behavior, including the problems arising from negative or disruptive behavior. Teachers who feel empowered are more likely to engage in problem-solving and respond in empathic, proactive ways, while those who do not feel empowered may feel frustrated and angry, and react in nonreflective ways, thinking there is no solution to the problem.

When faced with challenging behaviors, it is normal to feel frustration when nothing you try seems to work. At the point you give up, however, you become resigned to the situation, which may increase your frustration, impede your ability to respond empathically and appropriately, and in turn result in more of the behavioral problem. You can try to change your attitudes and thoughts to a proactive, problem-solving mode. It is hoped that this manual will help to increase your feelings of empowerment by giving you methods for thinking empathically about and developing effective interventions for your classroom. A useful practice exercise for you might be to think of situations where you have felt powerless and finally found a solution that made you feel better about your skills (empowered) and made a positive difference for a child.

■ Case Study - Johnny

Johnny, enrolled in the third-grade class of Ms. Jones, is the topic of a conference between Ms. Jones and the district psychologist, Mr. Johnson.

Ms. Jones sighs heavily. "You know," she says, "I have tried everything I know how and nothing seems to penetrate. He won't pay attention, and can't seem to work on his own for even five minutes. He's always talking and disrupting the class. I don't know what to do anymore! I heard he's a 'crack' kid. There isn't much you can do with those kids. They don't know how to control themselves. If I didn't have thirty other children to think about, maybe I could help him, but I just can't spend so much time on one child. I have to consider the other children in my class. I've asked his mother to come to school, but I read in the folder she's got four younger kids at home. Who knows when she'll ever have time to show up. Maybe we could consider retention. That will get her attention!"

 *Points to Ponder*

Think about Ms. Jones' conversation, then think about the following questions:

1. How does Ms. Jones feel about her situation with Johnny?
2. How do YOU feel when you are in situations like Ms. Jones?
3. Why do you think she is feeling this way?
4. Why do you end up feeling as you do with children like Johnny?
5. What would you say to Ms. Jones to help her deal with Johnny's challenging behaviors?
6. What can you say to yourself that might change how you approach children like Johnny when they are in your classroom?

Discussion

In this case example, we see a situation in which the teacher is understandably frustrated in dealing with challenging behaviors. It would be important for Ms. Jones to try to develop a proactive, problem-solving attitude and begin to believe that there are other things to try with Johnny. Part of her frustration likely comes from the feeling that she is alone and has exhausted all the interventions she knows. It is likely that Ms. Jones will need to identify new sources to help her brainstorm and stimulate new ideas. Accessing the school psychologist, experienced colleagues, and special education teachers may all help in this effort to generate new ideas. These resource people can also help encourage positive, empowering self- statements. Strategizing ways to involve the parent(s) is another area that warrants brainstorming and a proactive stance.

Developmentally-Appropriate Practices

A central issue in considering behavioral problems is the effect developmentally appropriate tasks have on classroom behavior. In general, curricula are developed for the majority of children in a particular grade. Although the concept of developmentally appropriate practices is applicable for groups of children, it also is appropriate for the individual child. Children who have been exposed to drugs may need a child-specific program and the teacher must make adaptations. For example, if a task is too difficult for a child, negative behaviors such as inattention, disruptiveness, or engaging in irrelevant behaviors (e.g., making noises) may result. The teacher must be aware of the incompatibility of the task requirements and the child's ability in order to modify the requirements and thus minimize inappropriate behaviors.

Research has shown that a program developmentally appropriate to the needs and strengths of children significantly increases the level and rate of skills acquisition by preventing and/or reducing behaviors that interfere with learning. A developmentally appropriate curriculum is child-centered and family-focused and provides a safe and supportive environment that promotes the development of children.

The Components of a Developmentally Appropriate Program

- Curriculum goals

- Teaching strategies

- Integrated curriculum

- Prosocial behavior and social problem-solving

- Evaluation

Curriculum Goals

- The curriculum is designed to develop children's skills and begins at the level each child is at developmentally. It is planned and facilitated in direct correlation with a child's strengths, level of ability and learning style. The child is allowed to move at an individual pace in acquiring skills.

- The curriculum is integrated and horizontal in that traditional subjects are taught through thematic projects and activity centers. Teachers guide and support children's learning as they move through each experience. Rather than focusing on the past or future, each activity first comprehensively covers all that is in the child's present realm.

- Skills are taught as needed while children are engaging in project work. Direct instruction, modeling, cooperative learning among peers, and exploration are utilized as instructional strategies.

Teaching Strategies

- The majority of a teacher's time is spent designing and developing the environment and activities and determining how children's skill levels can be developed as they participate in guided activities. The teacher's and instructional assistants' roles are to facilitate learning by observing, engaging discussion, responding to questions, modeling, and challenging thinking.

- Materials and activities are relevant for children at various developmental levels. The type and level of instructional activity planned includes adequate simple and complex materials for children to manipulate and utilize in earning the required skills.

Integrated Curriculum

- The goal of the language and literacy program is to increase children's ability and willingness to communicate verbally and through reading and writing. Skills are taught as needed and viewed as means to these goals, rather than ends in themselves. Time is available for children to read, be read to, write, plan projects, do research, discuss, interview, and listen.

- Reading and math are integrated with other subject areas within activities. Math programs should center around discovery, problem solving and exploration utilizing a variety of manipulatives and instructional strategies.

- Social studies, health, and science concepts are learned through a variety of theme-based projects. These long-term projects include reading, researching, discussing and interviewing, problem-solving, planning, and working cooperatively. Many social studies and science lessons can be framed within the natural occurrences of daily living.

- Art, movement, and music can be integrated throughout the daily work of the children. While direct instruction of special subjects can be beneficial, children can learn to challenge and express themselves physically and aesthetically through participation in project work.

- Multicultural and multilingual activities and materials should be incorporated within projects. Teaching children to respect their families, values, and heritage is essential in building self-esteem.

Prosocial behavior and social problem-solving

- Cooperation, negotiation, and communication are important skills that can be taught within the daily classroom routine.

Evaluation

- Evaluation of children's progress is an ongoing process. Children should participate in the evaluation of their work and assist in analyzing where improvement is needed and what has been accomplished. Errors are viewed as an integral part of the learning process. Information gained from the evaluation session is incorporated into the future curriculum.

Teaching Prosocial Behavior

Prosocial behavior refers to the social and self-control skills a child needs to meet the demands encountered in school, home, and community. Developing prosocial behavior is an integral part of successful classroom management that provides long-lasting effects. Substance-exposed children often have not had an opportunity to learn social skills within their home environment. Drug-abusing families often do not offer feedback on behavior, or the feedback does not include what behavior would appropriately be substituted for the admonished behavior. Rules and consequences are often inconsistently administered. Children do not know what is socially appropriate and often do not know how to interact in a positive social manner. Thus the children lack the kinds of social problem-solving skills needed to guide them in making good choices as to how to behave. Interventions such as the Interpersonal Cognitive Problem Solving (ICPS) program (Shure and Spivack, 1988) can provide guidence for how to instill such skills in children who have these deficits. Prosocial programs such as those described by Ruth Sidney Charney (Teaching Children to Care) are also extremely helpful in helping the drug-exposed child develop social skills.

1. Emphasizes the need to provide opportunities for children to know one another and be known in the classroom.

   - Opportunities for children to be seen - notice what children do, bring into school, draw in pictures, like to do in "choice" periods

   - Opportunities for children to be heard and to hear one another - sharing news from home, stories from writing, work in process

   - Opportunities to be named and to name one another - greetings by teacher and classmates, naming games, names on morning charts, name cards and pictures on bulletin boards

   - Opportunities to be known - "The Self Curriculum:" booklets, journals, art work that describe family facts, likes, dislikes, events, wishes for the year to be shared with teacher and classmates. Classroom activities may include morning meeting, class meeting, "choice" periods, guided outdoor group games, language arts and social studies projects featuring "The Self Curriculum".

2. Generates and models class rules and guidelines for expected ethical behaviors:

   - The Golden Rule - children act out ways that they "bring the Golden Rule to school"

- One Rule - children think of "one rule" to make the classroom a place that is respectful and friendly

- Logical consequences - everyone forgets rules

- You break it - you fix it (apology, helping hand, etc.)

- Breach of faith - loss of privilege

- Choose not to participate - time out.

3. Models social situations and practices interpersonal problem-solving skills that can provide positive ways for children to assert their needs, resolve conflicts, and make friends by considering goals and developing options and their consequences.

   - "If someone calls you a name, what can you do?" " If you do that, what is likely to happen?"

   - "If you need something and someone is using it for a long time and won't let you use it, what can you do?" "If you do that, what is likely to happen?"

   - "If someone pushes you in line..."

   - "If you want someone to play with and you are afraid to ask..."

   - "If someone makes you very angry (very happy)..."

4. Models respect, friendliness, firmness of purpose, interest through teacher/student interactions by:

   - Showing children what you expect

   - Using affirming and encouraging language

   - Stressing the deed, not the doer

   - Noticing and commenting on what children do "right"

   - Redirecting behavior with a firm, kind manner

   - Saying what you mean, meaning what you say.

5. Provides opportunities to participate in cooperative group activities that encourage positive interdependence by:

   - Helping children learn ways to work together in small groups by dividing tasks, sharing ideas, complimenting efforts, etc

- Planning cooperative projects in various subject areas across the curriculum

- Organizing group games for fun, not competition

- Assigning clean-up crews.

6. Provides opportunities for children to learn constructive ways to handle controversy and differences through:

   - Current events debates

   - Different "right" solutions to the same problems

   - Class meetings to discuss and solve problems

   - Anti-bias curricula.

Proactive Approaches

When attempts to manage behavior are not complemented with teaching desired behavior, long-term benefit will be minimal (Kazdin, 1989). In fact, if control of behavior is achieved through punitive or negative approaches only, it is very possible that behavioral problems will escalate as the child retaliates. Our research has found that punitive or negative approaches of behavior management with drug-exposed children actually exacerbate the behavior.

When children do not behave as expected, the reasons may fall into one of two categories: performance deficits or skill deficits.

Performance Deficits

Performance deficits refer to those skills that a child has and knows how to perform, but, for any of a variety of reasons, does not. These reasons may include emotional problems, boredom, or that the undesired behaviors receive more reinforcement from peers or teachers than do the desired ones. Many children have the skills, but other interfering factors prevent the desired behaviors from being demonstrated. In order for you to address performance deficits, you must understand why the child is not performing as desired, respond empathically to this problem, and help the child understand that negative behaviors are inappropriate and more benefit will come from appropriate, or "prosocial," behaviors.

Performance deficits may be evidenced by highly variable behavior, such as when a child does well in one situation but not in another. It may be that the child has a performance deficit in the situation in which behavioral problems occur but is fine in another setting because it provides some ecological dimensions that are lacking elsewhere, such as level of structure, consistency, personal interest, etc. However, variability in performance may also be hiding a skill deficit due to the fact that the level of skill required for success in one setting is not adequate for another setting. For example, the child may demonstrate skills when someone is working with him directly in a one-to-one situation, but when he left to complete the same material on his own he is unable to do so because of organizational deficits. Therefore, the distinction between performance and skill deficits can sometimes be quite difficult to assess. However, it is important to make this distinction because your teaching approach will be different for skill deficits as compared with performance deficits.

In general, the proactive approach to addressing a performance deficit is to identify an alternative, desired behavior and try to strengthen it through teaching, positive reinforcement, and helping the child feel good about her appropriate behavior. At the same time, you should de-emphasize or ignore the undesired behavior. We realize that ignoring some behaviors is not always possible in the classroom. In those cases, you may have to use techniques to suppress the behavior while you continue to emphasize a proactive/prosocial approach.

Skill Deficits

Skill deficits refer to the child's not having the skills needed to perform the desired tasks. Reasons for skill deficits include faulty teaching and modeling at home, reinforcement for inappropriate instead of appropriate behaviors, or lack of opportunity to learn the desired skills. Some substance-exposed children may enter school without encountering such simple background experiences as hearing stories or rhymes, learning colors and numbers, or naming the objects in their environment. Some vulnerable or high-risk children, including those prenatally exposed to drugs, may have more difficulty learning certain types of skills that are needed for prosocial behavior due to impulsivity, low frustration tolerance, and a tendency toward disorganized behavior.

For skill deficits, your challenge is to determine what the specific deficits are and find ways to teach and develop them. You should also remember that what you assume to be a performance deficit, in fact, may be a skill deficit. The child may not be intentionally misbehaving; he may not know how to do what is appropriate. The behavior he exhibits is what he knows how to do, and it may have negative consequences.

For some children skill deficits may be rather small and need little remediation, while others may need much more effort. For example, the prenatally exposed boy who has difficulty lining up to go to lunch may need to be physically walked through the process several times until it becomes an automatic part of his repertoire. The girl who cannot keep herself organized to complete work when she does not have someone working with her needs extra help to organize her work initially, and then regular check-ins from the teacher to ensure that she has kept herself on track. Identification and remediation of skill deficits often will correct and eliminate many problem behaviors because the child will now know what to do and what is expected, especially when given well-placed reminders and a lot of positive reinforcement and praise.

Management vs. Control

Throughout this book, we emphasize the importance of distinguishing "management" and "control." When many people talk about classroom management, they implicitly or explicitly may equate it with maintaining control of the classroom. Control may be interpreted to mean that the goal is to suppress or contain undesirable behavior so instruction can continue in an orderly manner. We need to empower children to take control of their lives by facilitating their development, not controlling it. Often we spend all our time developing ways to externally control the behavior of children when what the children need are adults who will help empower through respect, listening, collaboration and problem solving approaches.

In this book, we define management as "maintaining classroom activities while teaching appropriate behavior." We hope you will see the link between the previous discussion of prosocial behavior and its relationship to other important components of effective classroom management: providing structure, predictability and consistency.

For children who have been prenatally exposed to drugs and present difficulties in the classroom, prosocial behavior, structure, predictability, and consistency may be lacking in their homes. However, even if these attributes are present in the home, they are equally important in the school and the classroom. These dimensions help all children succeed in school but are especially critical for prenatally exposed children. A stable school environment that helps them know what they are expected to do and how to go about doing it (structure); a classroom in which they know what their day will look like and how school personnel will respond to them (predictability); and an environment where responses to the children are the same every day (consistency) can make a major difference in how prenatally exposed children behave and are most useful in enhancing their prosocial behavior.

Let us revisit the conversation between Ms. Jones, the third-grade teacher frustrated by Johnny's behavior, and Mr. Johnson, the school psychologist whom she has consulted for help.

Case Study - Johnny: Revisiting Ms. Jones

Since her last visit, Mr. Johnson, the school psychologist, has helped Ms. Jones feel more empowered to deal with Johnny's behavior by providing opportunity to brainstorm and think of new ideas. Now, they are discussing Johnny's impulsive and wild behavior on the playground.

■ Case Study - Johnny

"It seems like every day he gets into trouble," states Ms. Jones. "He starts running and then can't stop. Within a few minutes he's running wildly and screaming. Sometimes he pushes other children when they are in his way. I have no choice but to take him back inside and punish him. When I do that, though, he sulks for the rest of the day and won't participate in any of the group activities. I tried taking away recess but no matter how many times I do, he does the same thing again the next time he goes out. Nobody wants to play with him anymore because he has to control the play activity, which leads to conflicts and then gets them into trouble."

 Points to Ponder

1. Do you think Ms. Jones was effective in trying to manage Johnny's behavior? Why or why not?

2. If Johnny were in your class, how might you manage his behavior?

Ms. Jones' use of external threats and confinement to interrupt Johnny's behavior was unsuccessful. The descriptions of Johnny's behavior suggest he tends to display undercontrolled behavior and has difficulty organizing himself, so Ms. Jones attempted to control him by keeping him inside. Although it may be necessary to remove him from a situation temporarily, he does not seem to be learning anything from it because he often repeats the pattern. This is the problem with strategies aimed at controlling behavior rather than managing it so that the child learns how to act appropriately and learns self-control.

Recess can often be an extremely difficult time for children with the kind of regulatory problems often displayed by drug-exposed children. The combination of excitement and lack of structure can make it very difficult for them to calm down and organize their behavior. Think *prevention*. Discuss expectations for recess behavior at length prior to letting Johnny out onto the playground. Set a clear plan for what he would like to do during recess and who he would like to play with so there is structure for his activity. Talk through what his behavior should look like during recess and what you will do if you notice his behavior is not in keeping with his stated plan. At such a time, Johnny should be removed from the situation or behavior in which he is engaged and provided an alternative spot in which to calm down until he appears ready to manage and organize his behavior again, with repetition of the prevention plan discussed in the classroom. Give Johnny large amounts of praise as he becomes increasingly successful in managing himself. In the long run, Johnny may even be able to take himself out of situations when he is beginning to feel out of control, so he can give himself a "break" and put himself back in control of himself.

Contrasting control vs. management of behavior

The concept of behavior management versus control is simple but important. Teachers should teach children to manage their own behavior through self-control, responsibility, and social skills, just as they teach them subject matter such as reading and mathematics. Returning to the case of Johnny, Ms. Jones continues her discussion with the school psychologist. Trying to understand factors that may have contributed to Johnny's behavior, the psychologist asks about that morning in the classroom.

Behavior	Control	Management
Johnny gets into fights.	Keep Johnny inside during recess.	Talk through the expected behavior with Johnny before recess. Create a plan for behavior and activity during recess, with a model for what he should do if he feels himself getting into trouble with other children.
Johnny gets up and wanders around the room.	Keep Johnny in his seat.	Make sure the work given is clearly organized and structured. Set a time limit for how long Johnny is expected to work (10 minutes, for example), then permit a short break before he returns for another 10-minute work session.
Johnny has to control the activity.	Keep Johnny from offending peers.	Coach the class before group work or play when playing or working with peers about sharing and control. Review expectations for behavior. Check on Johnny regularly to provide extra coaching.
Johnny pushes his classmates when he's in line.	Stop Johnny from hitting.	Place Johnny at the front or the end of the line so he is not between two children. Coach class on what to say if other children are too close to them, and help everyone understand the different levels of tolerance for personal space.
Johnny withdraws when he feels he cannot succeed in the task.	Keep Johnny from withdrawing.	Discuss the goal of learning versus the success/failure in the classroom work. Never use humiliation when the child cannot perform. Set up rotating participation so everyone has to contribute. Teach the class how to support their peers' learning efforts.

■ Case Study - Johnny

"Everything went smoothly this morning until I took the first reading group," Ms. Jones recalls. *"The children were working on seatwork exercises. Johnny got up and started walking around the classroom, disturbing the others. I told him to sit down and do his work and he said he didn't know how. I had just spent at least thirty minutes going over the assignment with the class! I told him that he would have to leave the room, so I put him in the hallway and closed the door. He started making noises through the vent. I called the office and asked the principal to send someone to get him. Later, when Johnny was returned to class, he hit another child because he said he broke his pencil. I sent him to time out to sit alone in the corner. I'm afraid I lost my temper and told him that if he didn't want to learn I didn't care what he did as long as he didn't bother anyone else. I said I wouldn't bother to even try to teach him. Then he started making quacking noises while he sat in the corner, distracting the other children from story time. I told him that his punishment was to write a full-page essay on ducks for homework and have it signed by his mother. I really don't know what to do with him anymore. I have tried every punishment I know, and he doesn't seem to care!"*

Points to Ponder

1. Why do you think Ms. Jones believes that Johnny is acting out? What other reasons might there be for his behavior?

   Ms. Jones appears to think Johnny is acting out in order to bother her or the class. However, there are many other possibilities to explain this behavior, including that Johnny is frustrated because he may not know how to do the assignment or that he is having difficulty focusing on the task because of a distraction in the classroom or problems at home.

2. What was the first indication that Johnny was having difficulty managing himself? What do you think Ms. Jones could have done to more successfully manage Johnny's behavior?

   The first indication that Johnny was having difficulty managing himself came when he left his seat and began to walk around the classroom. Ms. Jones at that point could have checked to see that he understood and remembered the assignment. He also may not have known how to organize the assignment if it were not highly structured. Ms. Jones could have paired Johnny with another child who understood the assignment; she could have had him sit with her; she could have given him alternate seatwork. Other helpful techniques would be to plan classroom activities differently, setting up more cooperative learning projects during reading group time so children can work together on assignments.

In this situation, the teacher clearly feels frustrated and unempowered and is using techniques to suppress and control behavior. However, as indicated, there is evidence that Johnny may not have known how to do the exercises and could not manage the frustration and tension created by this situation. Although Ms. Jones stated that she had explained the exercises, Johnny said he did not know how to do them. Ms. Jones seems to be assuming Johnny is willfully not doing something he knows how to do (a performance deficit), when a skill deficit is a more likely explanation and will certainly lead to different interventions and responses. The important things that would have likely led to less escalation of problems include:

1. Listening carefully to Johnny's communication and responding in a way that lets him know he has been "heard."

2. Recognizing that not all challenging behavior is intentional acting out in pursuit of attention for attention's sake.

3. Recognizing that not all children operate at the same level and respond to formal explanations and directions in the same way.

4. Remembering that there may be more than one explanation for a child's behavior.

5. Acknowledging the constant need for the teacher to balance his responsibilities to the class as a whole and the special needs of specific children. Recognizing a child's needs with a promise to help as soon as possible can be quite helpful, when provided in a consistent and predictable way.

6. Finally, the most important intervention is the one that occurs before any problem arises: in the planning and organizing classroom activities and preparing the children for such activities.

Classroom Management

Many classroom management situations can exacerbate or escalate children's difficulties with self-management:

- Using punitive approaches too often and/or without accompanying positive approaches.

- Absent, ambiguous, or inconsistently enforced classroom rules..

- Inadvertent reinforcement of undesirable behavior.

- Failure to recognize or reinforce desirable behavior when it occurs.

- Behavior or practices/policies that serve to embarrass, denigrate, humiliate, or intimidate a child, i.e., threats, negative comments about ability or characteristics, especially in the presence of peers, inappropriately ignoring the child's needs, or forms of corporal punishment.

- Lack of a recognizable, comprehensive, and effective plan for helping children learn how to manage their behavior.

Much of what is written and practiced in the classroom involves addressing emotional and behavioral problems that have a long history and may require direct interventions to modify them in the classroom. However, another important aspect of addressing problems is to learn more about preventing their occurrence in the first place. In general, it is much more effective to prevent problems than it is to respond to them after they have emerged. There are two principles of preventive behavior management: promoting positive, desired behaviors, and minimizing behaviors that are disruptive to the instructional process. The classroom that is prevention- focused will use procedures and techniques that focus on both components.

Proactive management techniques are important for the teacher because there is evidence that they may prevent up to 75% of disruptive student behavior. Prevention efforts may include reviewing environmental and instructional variables in the classroom. It should be remembered, however, that even in the best-managed classrooms, where sound prevention practices are evident, problem behaviors will nevertheless occur.

The Classroom Environment

There are a number of events or circumstances in the classroom itself that can contribute to the occurrence of certain behaviors, including group arrangement, internal and external disruptions, sudden changes in activities, and less-than-adequate monitoring of student behavior.

While every teacher has many children to monitor, the kinds of classroom interventions described in this section will meet the needs of both those children who respond to traditional classroom management techniques, and those who don't. The critical first step is to watch your students carefully, note when they seem to have the most difficulty — transitions, after a loudspeaker announcement, during group activities or during independent work. You will have to tune in to the cues your students provide and remember to interpret their meaning and think about their function, rather than simply trying to extinguish them. Once you've engaged in this process you are in a position to think about your classroom, its organization, the structure of the day and your intervention and management efforts in new ways that address the communications children are providing in their behavior.

Many teachers are concerned that they have to spend too much time dealing with a couple of "special" children in their class, resulting in their neglect of the other students. However, the best way to conserve time and energy for all your students is to be proactive in reducing the problems created by those few students by preventing the behaviors in the first place. This will give you more time and increase your availability to the class as a whole, as well as provide you more time to teach. It is in waiting for the inevitable problem to arise, and then reacting to it, that your attention is diverted, the classroom is disrupted, and the learning comes to a halt.

Communicating Desired Behaviors

How often have you heard someone or you yourself say, "You know better than that!" to a child? As adults we tend to assume that children have been taught what is acceptable and what is not acceptable behavior, but that often is not the case. Children who live in drug-using environments do not get much helpful feedback on their behavior. When we work with children we must not only tell them what we don't want them to do, but be very specific about why that behavior is unacceptable and what would be acceptable in that circumstance. Use clearly stated rules and expectations so your students know what you want, i.e., the behaviors that will earn them positive results and those that will not. Although telling students what you want is a logical method, there are a number of other ways to communicate with them.

Communicating Desired Behaviors

To communicate desired behaviors:

- *post a chart of classroom rules.*
- *remind class of rules when an individual child breaks a rule.*
- *write notes to students when they follow the rules.*
- *write notes to parents when children are meeting your expectations.*
- *provide frequent feedback to students about their behavior.*
- *show nonverbal looks, gazes, expressions and gestures following a desired behavior.*

Establishing Classroom Rules

Establishing and enforcing classroom rules and behavioral expectations are important preventive measures. They provide clarity and consistency for what the child can expect from the teacher and what he is expected to do. It has been found that children generally respect rules that they make, and they learn more from rules that are positive. Rules should encourage reason and thinking and provoke active discussion. Young children in the kindergarten and primary levels want to please adults and be seen as "good" in their eyes. Teachers should be careful to apply the right measure of discipline when rules are broken. If the teacher's response is too harsh, the child may experience such a sense of shame and guilt that his initiative and sense of autonomy is affected. On the other hand, responses that are too weak could result in the child's not understanding how to control himself. For older children, starting in second and third grade, rules are based on the well-being of the social community. Issues of fairness, ethics and the well being of others are discussed. Children are now able to see rules that apply beyond themselves to the needs of the group and understand why such rules are reasonable and necessary.

Fair and consistent rules are helpful in establishing a sense of order and control in the classroom. Substance-exposed children come from environments in which the out-of-control parent creates a world that is unpredictable and uncertain. The establishment of classroom rules allows substance-affected children to develop a sense of control over their lives.

Negatively stated rules imply an expectation of misbehavior, although they tend to be easier to state than positive rules. Negatively stated rules should be avoided, and should be used only for fairly innocuous and routine situations, such as, "Don't bring toys to school."

Establishing Classroom Rules

Classroom rules should be:

- *made and discussed with the children. Focus on why rules are needed.*
- *made to serve a purpose.*
- *stated in very clear, specific and concrete behavioral terms, e.g., rather than say "be nice to each other," a rule might say "take turns in group." Children should know when they are following a rule and when they are breaking a rule.*
- *limited to no more than six (the fewer the better): they should be posted and easy to read.*
- *stated in positive terms because they communicate positive expectations. Say what we do, not what we don't do.*
- *discussed to see how they relate to daily routines and activities.*
- *reviewed on a regular basis, e.g., every two weeks, and whenever a rule is violated by several members of the class.*
- *introduced with each activity to remind students of expectations.*

Be consistent in what is expected and in how rules are enforced. If you have a rule that requires a child to raise his hand before speaking but then do not enforce it when he speaks without permission, inconsistency results and the power of the rule is undermined. If a child violates a rule, it should be discussed with him to assure he understands it. Reminders or corrective statements for an individual should be done in private, so as not to humiliate the child. The group may be reminded of a high level of group infractions, but individual children should not be identified. It is important to reinforce individuals and groups for exceptional compliance with the rules by offering a special activity or reward.

Establishing a Reward System

As you begin establishing a reward system, you may want to keep in mind that interruptions in expected rewards often cause uncertainty and confusion for younger children. If it becomes difficult to give rewards after positive behavior, then your procedures should be reviewed and revised.

- At first, reinforcement should be given each time a desired behavior occurs. Plan to gradually decrease the amount of reinforcement expected.

- The child should be reminded why she is receiving the reward.

- Even if a tangible reward is not given each time, social rewards such as praise can be given.

- For younger children or children who exhibit negative behaviors often, frequency of reward for appropriate behavior is important.

- Minimize rewards for inappropriate or undesired behavior.

Although it may seem difficult to imagine that anyone would reward undesired behavior, such events occur frequently. It is important to remember that what is rewarding for one child is not rewarding for another. For example, if a child misbehaves, the attention received from an adult may be rewarding for the attention-hungry child, increasing the chances for repeating the behavior.

When undesired behaviors are rewarded, observe the reaction of the child to determine if the behavior increases. If so, review your approach and consider how to respond to that child if the situation recurs. Ignore mild occurrences of disruptive or negative behavior, if possible, which will help to reduce problems by removing rewarding attention. Extremely disruptive or dangerous behavior may not be able to be ignored, however, and should be addressed.

First identify rewards that the children can try to earn. It is important to remember that what may be rewarding for an adult or older child may not be so for the young child. Develop a list of rewards that your students like by asking them, observing their behavior, and talking with colleagues.

Establishing Rewards

Rewards should be:

- *logical and natural for the classroom environment.*
- *changed and varied, with higher requirements for rewards that are more highly valued, e.g., free time.*
- *very specific, familiar and perceived to be attainable by the students.*
- *social as well as tangible (smiles, praise, privilege, recognition, etc.).*
- *given consistently for positive behavior.*
- *given each time a desired behavior occurs. Plan to gradually decrease the amount of reinforcement expected.*
- *minimized for inappropriate or undesired behavior.*

Creating a Consistent and Predictable Classroom Environment

Establishing daily routines and habits can have a preventive effect in the classroom. A predictable routine and schedule assists children in understanding and trusting their environment. Having clear expectations that are actualized will reduce the anxiety children have with ordering and organizing their own world - whether at school or at home.

School-age substance-exposed children often have self-regulation problems that are similar to the state regulation problems seen in infancy. It is not that they can't self-regulate; they need environments that help them stay below their threshold of stimulation and help in developing self-regulation strategies.

Our clinical observations lead us to believe that loss of behavioral control or withdrawal in substance-exposed children can be triggered by a number of environmental situations and stimuli. In fact, anything that increases the inconsistency and decreases the predictability of the child's environment will exacerbate the self-regulatory problems of children. Substance-exposed children have a hard time coping with transitions and changes in their lives. They may often display adequate regulatory abilities in familiar environments but lose this ability when presented with a new circumstance or situation. The first step toward helping children learn to regulate is to provide them with consistent and predictable environments. With stable routines, rules, discipline, and nurturance they know what to expect from those around them. This confidence in their environment frees them to concentrate on controlling internal states of arousal and impulses. When the children are exposed to new environments or new tasks, it is helpful to anticipate their problems and help them maintain control by providing one-on-one attention, guidance and structure.

Daily Schedule

Changes to the schedule should be avoided. If the day needs to follow a different schedule, each activity should be facilitated but shortened. The daily schedule or structure of a normal school day can be overstimulating for the child with a low threshold for stimulation. Variations such as fire drills, schedule changes, assemblies and programs, switching teachers or classrooms or attending special classes can produce anxiety and distrust in these children. Administrators should carefully assess the intended and actual value of schedule changes for children who have difficulty in adjusting to new situations.

Establishing a Daily Schedule

- *Alternate activities every 20 to 30 minutes.*
- *Alternate activities between quiet and active types.*
- *Allow for burn-up-energy activities.*
- *Post daily/weekly calendar. Go over daily schedule.*
- *Have children keep own schedule and cross off activities when finished.*
- *Closure at the end of the day. Discuss next day/prepare for what happens tomorrow.*
- *Open and closing activities.*
- *Post schedule in words and pictures.*
- *Try to have the same schedules every day (be predictable).*

Stable Routines

Routines and habits are particularly important for transitions between activities. Managing transitions can be extremely difficult for some children, and those at risk because of factors such as prenatal or environmental drug exposure are especially vulnerable. Children who are drug-exposed need to know what to expect and what is expected of them. Not only does this give them a sense of control over their lives, but if their external environment is consistent and predicable their energy can be used to manage themselves internally.

Transitions

Transitions are times in which change is required, and substance-exposed children do not react well to change. Transitions are often unstructured, can be disorganized, and rarely follow a set routine. Children who need a great deal of structure or have difficulty regulating their behavior in a chaotic or less-organized situation will become lost as they move from one activity or setting to another. Routines help keep children occupied and involved and are associated with enhanced achievement..

Teachers report that the primary time that challenging, inappropriate behaviors occur is during transition. They have also found that these behaviors decrease greatly or are even prevented if simple strategies are applied.

Establish Routines For Transitions By:

- *introducing the structure of transition time to the children (i.e., just like any other activity, it has a beginning, middle, and end).*
- *alternating the daily schedule in a developmentally appropriate way, with active and quiet, large and small, group and individual activity time.*
- *providing clear cues or warnings to signal when transition will soon begin, actually begin, and end (music, color codes, timers, visual cues such a lights on and off).*
- *reviewing the routine of transition before it is to begin (preview the transition).*
- *showing each step of the transition process (through instruction, peer support, role modeling, etc.) for children who require a great deal of structured guidance.*

Preparing children for transitions should include any change that will affect the child's schedule and routine. If possible plan ahead for substitute teachers, forewarning children of an impending teacher absence whenever possible. Children should be prepared for schedule changes. In the case of such things as fire drills, room changes, and assemblies children should have the opportunity to practice these situations

There remains a tendency in some classrooms to try to get the child to fit the typical routine, rather than fit the routine to the child. This is not to say that routines and practices that are set up for the group necessarily are inappropriate for drug-exposed children, but it may be that modifications in these procedures must be made to meet their unique needs. Often, a small gesture as simple and easy as a hand on the shoulder will be sufficient.

Physical Arrangement of the Classroom

The classroom is the environment in which you interact with your students and where most learning occurs. You can make several choices about its appearance and physical arrangement and how you set the tone for activities that take place. Research has shown that appropriate arrangement of the classroom can promote appropriate behavior and prevent behavior problems. Specifically, it is important that the classroom be orderly and reassuring. You can organize the physical space of the classroom in a way that reduces distractions and confusion.

Classroom Organization

Substance-exposed children who have difficulty organizing themselves within their environment often require the teacher to present the framework through which that organization can take place. Such things as learning centers, bulletin boards, posters and other materials can be distracting for such children unless they have some context. Let us return to Ms. Jones and Mr. Johnson to illustrate this point:

■ Case Study - Johnny

Ms. Jones asks Mr. Johnson to recommend that Johnny's medication dosage be increased. She points out that his behavior is much worse in the afternoon than in the morning and he is constantly disruptive in class. Mr. Johnson asks for an example of this behavior. "Well," answers Ms. Jones, "this morning we went to the aquarium on a field trip. When we returned this afternoon, we had a group discussion about porpoises. Our discussion was very active and the class was participating beautifully when suddenly Johnny cried out, 'We have "Charlotte's Web" at home!, You can imagine what happened then. The class went up for grabs and it took me half an hour to get them all back on track. It's not like this is the first time, you know. He is disruptive and gets everyone else off task with him!"

Discussion of Case Study - Johnny

Mr. Johnson continues to ask Ms. Jones questions about the circumstances of Johnny's distraction. Although Ms. Jones had first characterized Johnny's behavior as a "discipline problem," he leads her to understand that Johnny was having a distractibility problem. Ms. Jones tells Mr. Johnson that she had received a "Charlotte's Web" poster in the mail the previous afternoon and put it up in the classroom with no discussion or explanation accompanying it.

Mr. Johnson explains that Johnny, whose mind started to wander during the porpoise discussion, started looking around the classroom. His attention was caught by something that had no contextual meaning to him, his brain tried to make sense of it so he processed it within the only context he had. Johnny mind-connected the poster of "Charlotte's Web" to the video he had at home and, because of his high rate of impulsivity, he blurted out this association for all to hear. Mr. Johnson explains that Johnny was actually processing information quite well. However, he should be made aware of how disruptive his impulsive behavior is to his classmates. Johnny's medication is not increased, and Ms. Jones resolves not to put things into the classroom environment without first introducing them and putting them in a context for the children.

Arranging the Classroom Environment

When arranging your classroom environment you should:

- *label classroom materials and spaces, outline their locations.*
- *make neat, purposeful learning centers that are not overstimulating and are easily accessible for both simple and complex materials. Use decorations that can be easily removed in case they become distracting.*
- *introduce and clearly define the purpose of visual stimuli, e.g., bulletin boards, learning centers, decorations. Organize around themes.*
- *clearly define work spaces and mark their boundaries.*
- *provide private areas and soft elements such as pillows and rugs, rocking chairs, headphones, etc.*
- *provide individual space for each student's belongings.*
- *clearly identify and mark materials. Keep clutter to a minimum.*
- *limit distractions - ensure adequate light, ventilation.*
- *provide a "time out," or "calm down" or "alone" space where children can go to regain their organization, balance and self-control.*

Classroom Seating

Often availability of resources, arrangement of furniture, and physical access to activities and materials limit your control over classroom density. Crowding tends to contribute to decreased attention, social withdrawal, aggressiveness, dissatisfaction, and nervousness.However, you can reduce the negative effects of density and crowding by changing the size of groups in the classroom (social density) and by placing same-size groups in different-size spaces (spatial density).

In cooperative learning situations, group seating arrangements may lead to better performance than row seating. Students who sit in circles or clusters tend to have better on-task behavior but students who sit in circles make more on-task comments. Circular seating arrangements produce fewer disruptions than row seating. While row seating is the best method for lecture and material presentation, it is not appropriate for most other activities.

Alternate Seating Arrangements

Circular Seating

- *Students who sit in circles make more on-task comments*
- *Fewer disruptions occur in circular arrangements*

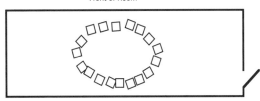

Horseshoe, U-shaped Seating

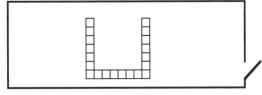

Cluster Seating

- *Students who sit in clusters or circles tend to have better on-task behavior.*

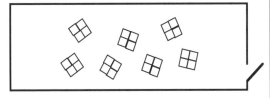

Row Seating

- *Row seating is the best method for lecture and material presentation.*

Front of Room

Group Approaches to Classroom Management

Although much of what is written about classroom management tends to focus on addressing individual behavioral problems by using reinforcement or punishment procedures, we believe that management techniques should start with two types of intervention. The first type, a group approach, involves assessing current classroom environment, circumstances, and management practices to determine if problems exist that can be corrected by modifying the classroom environment or situation. For example, if a child becomes off task because the assignment is too difficult, making changes so that the child can complete it successfully may eliminate the problem. This group approach to intervention is discussed in this section. The second type is the individual intervention, which involves more systematic procedures and the use of a problem-solving process that addresses the child's behavior on an individual level. At this level much more detailed and focused interventions are developed. This second type of invervention will be developed and discussed in the next section of this manual.

Scanning

Scanning refers to the teacher's maintaining frequent visual monitoring of classroom activities, particularly those in which students work independently. Failing to scan usually results in teachers responding only to misbehavior, leading to difficulties with communicating behavioral expectations. Scanning is related to what is termed "withitness," the ability to know what is happening in the classroom, which leads to prevention of behavior problems. Maintaining eye contact with students, often without verbal comments, is an effective way to prevent misbehavior.

Group management

Group management approaches can help with the behaviors of individual children, as well as the larger group. A classroom in which the teacher regularly employs group management approaches is likely to have fewer behavioral problems. Although you will probably develop many behavioral interventions for individual children, group management approaches may be effective in reducing or preventing misbehavior or academic problems. If implemented correctly, they can be more effective than some individual interventions. The positive effectiveness of group contingencies over individual interventions rests on the power of peer pressure. Peers control much approval and praise, as well as negative consequences, such as threats and social rejection.

Contingencies

Contingencies is a central concept to effective classroom management, although its meaning may be unclear. The best synonym for the term is "dependent" and refers to the relationship of one event to another. If there is a contingent relationship between two events, then one is a result of (i.e., dependent upon) the occurrence of the other. For example, your receiving a paycheck is contingent (dependent) upon your working. A child receives an "A" grade contingent upon doing the necessary work. A child receives a reward contingent upon whether he or she completes a task for which a reward has been promised.

Many teachers (and parents) are uncomfortable with the idea of using rewards to help children manage their behavior, equating the use of such a contingency to that of a bribe. But using such incentives or consequences are very powerful interventions that provide the message: "You (the student) are in charge of what happens, I am not controlling you — it's up to you." Thus, the teacher, rather than being the punitive provider of punishments, becomes the coach who can empower the child to see that he can exert control and manage himself. Positive incentives are an especially useful tool with children who are oppositional and defiant. Incentives are also a way to acknowledge that you are asking a child to do something that is difficult for her. It is no different from the kinds of incentives and bonuses provided to adults in the workplace when employers want more productivity, e.g., the promise of a promotion or raise. When you offer an incentive for successful execution of something that you understand requires much effort, you are providing an empathic intervention that lets a child know you understand him and do not blame him.

Incentives and contingencies also help children who tend to be impulsive by helping them think before they act. If the wish to act (i.e., hit another child) and the action itself are essentially simultaneous, the child is not in a position to make a different choice (i.e., walk away). Incentives help a child put a couple of beats between the wish to act and the action (i.e., "If I hit this kid, I'll lose my sticker"), and thus help build her capacity for self-control by having successful experiences.

Using these types of interventions also allows the teacher to be very creative and involved with his students. What motivates the children in one's classroom? How can the contingency be structured? How can the children work together to meet extra goals? But remember, the

73

chosen contingency must be meaningful to the child — that is, it must be something she wants, so it will provide the motivation and incentive she needs to reach the targeted goal.

There are many examples of establishing contingencies or relationships in managing behavior. In fact, the large majority of everyday behavior is a product of the contingencies established among events or objects. We all receive rewards or positive consequences as a function of our behavior, e.g., a "thank you" for helping someone with a problem. We can also receive negative consequences for inappropriate behavior, e.g., receiving a traffic ticket for speeding. Obviously then, not all contingencies are positive. A child can get attention for misbehavior. For example, a child who acts aggressively may get attention from a subset of his peers. Thus, getting the attention is contingent upon being aggressive. A contingency by itself is neither positive nor negative, but it is the nature of the relationship that is important.

The idea of contingencies can also be viewed as logical consequences when teaching children to take responsibility for their own behavior. This notion of logical consequences is most effective with drug-exposed children because it reinforces the idea of self-regulation and puts children in charge of themselves by encouraging them to examine their own behaviors and think about the choices they make. By doing so they are able to regain their self-control and their self-respect.

Guidelines for Logical Consequences

Some guidelines for logical consequences (Charney)

- *Logical consequences are respectful of the student and classroom. Students give input into possible consequences including choices about specifics of consequences. Logical consequences are not intended to humiliate or hurt.*

- *Logical consequences need to respond to choices and actions, not character. The message is that misbehavior results from poor judgment or bad planning but not from poor character.*

- *Logical consequences need to be put into practice with both empathy and structure. Empathy shows our knowledge of children and our willingness to hear what they have to say; structure establishes and provide appropriate directions. The teacher needs to be firm and kind. Kindness shows our respect for the child; firmness shows respect for oneself.*

(continued on next page...)

- *Logical consequences should be used to describe the demands of the situation, not the demands of the authority. This helps avoid power struggles.*

- *Logical consequences should be used only after the teacher has assessed the situation. Misbehaviors may result from expectations that are not appropriate to the developmental needs of children, or from expectations incompatible with an individual's particular needs. The best alternative may be to restructure the environment and readjust the expectations. When confronted with misbehavior, there are two questions to ask:*

  a) Are my expectations appropriate to the age needs of the group?
  b) Are my expectations appropriate to the individual needs and abilities of the student?

- *Stop and think before imposing logical consequences. Teachers often need time to think not just to react.*

- *Logical consequences help to restore self-control and self-respect because self-respect demands not just words, but actions.*

■   *All logical consequences need to be implemented with both empathy and structure. Empathy preserves the dignity of the child. Structure preserves the dignity of the classroom. (Charney)*

Example

■ Example of Ronnie:

Ronnie is a first-grader who has difficulty completing all the seat work given due to some visual-motor difficulties as well as attentional deficits that make it hard for him to copy the 10 sentences from the board assigned by the teacher. When the rest of the class has completed the assignment, Ronnie is still on sentence 5. Despite suggestions by the learning disabilities teacher and an outside psychologist, Ronnie's teacher refused to modify the number of sentences Ronnie had to copy in order to receive credit for completion. Ronnie was frustrated and displayed considerable disruptive behavior in this academic situation.

 *Points to Ponder*

1. What logical consequences is the teacher using?

2. Why is this likely to backfire?

Comments: Ronnie

This teacher had a clearly defined policy that no child could be exempted from the expected work in her classroom as this would undermine her structure and authority. But what did the teacher and Ronnie gain from this rule - what logical consequences is she applying? Ronnie still did not complete his assignment, undermining his sense of competence and making him more angry and frustrated, leading to behavioral problems that required the teacher's attention and energy. If, on the other hand, the teacher had considered the logical repercussions of reducing Ronnie's assignment, Ronnie would have been successful both in completing the assignment and in managing himself. The teacher would have been able to give him positive feedback and not have to engage in more intrusive behavior management techniques. Thus, despite the wish to use rules equally for all students, the logical consequences of those rules can have results that clearly undermine the success of both the child and the classroom.

Discussion

Logical expectations with logical consequences will always work better than arbitrary rules that do not take into consideration the differing needs of children in the classroom. While teachers may initially believe that adapting assignments for individual children will make more work for them, these preventive efforts almost always save time and energy later, and provide everyone a sense of competence and success.

Implementation of Logical Consequences

There are a number of different methods for using contingencies for the entire classroom. There are advantages and disadvantages for each method. It is critical that the goals sought by using one of these strategies be carefully considered before implementing any one of them.

Implementing Logical Consequences (Charney)

• *Stop and think.*

• *Evaluate the options.*

• *Provide a workable, realistic, specific action as a consequence.*

• *Provide a time limit.*

• *Emphasize the language of "choice" and "privilege."*

• *Use empathy and structure.*

Interdependent Group Contingencies

In this approach, the behavior of some children determines whether the entire class receives a reward. If one or more children misbehave beyond acceptable criteria, none of the children will receive a reward. Therefore, the children may exert social pressure on one another to accomplish a goal as a group. For example, the teacher may tell the students that, if all of them can get at least 80% on all assignments, they can have a party at the end of the week. This technique can be particularly effective and is seen in methods such as cooperative learning, where the group works for a common goal and shares reinforcers. This method is most effective when children get together to establish meaningful rewards.

In this method, access to rewards is contingent upon the behavior of a single child or subgroup, rather than upon the entire group. For example, if a specific child is observed to be behaving appropriately, the entire class is given a reward (positive reinforcement). If the same child is observed not to be behaving appropriately, the class is not given a reward (nonreinforcement) or may lose rewards (response cost).

Dependent Group Contingencies

While this traditional method of contingencies is often used for behavior modification, it needs to be used very cautiously. It is imperative that the identified behaviors are ones that the child has clearly mastered — that is there is no skill deficit, and you have established that the child can perform the behavior in the situation you are setting up. If this has not been established, then you may be setting up the child for failure, as well as setting him up to receive the anger and disappointment of his peers. The relationship between prenatal substance exposure and behavior has been substantiated by our research. The children may exhibit behaviors that are inadvertent; thus using techniques such as dependent group contingencies could easily have a very negative effect on the child whose behavior is not willful but a result of neurological injury.

Mystery Child

A variation on this technique is the "mystery child" method where a child is selected by the teacher, who observes the child at random intervals. The entire class is told that a "mystery child" is being observed, but the class will not know who it is. If the child is behaving appropriately when the teacher observes, then the entire class receives a reward or credit toward a more valued activity, such as a class party on Friday afternoon. The advantages of this approach are several: the children think it's fun; since they don't know who is under scrutiny, they all tend to behave better; and the reward or (non-reward) serves as reinforcement for good behavior. The procedure should involve several observations per day (e.g., 6 to 8), in order to sustain the children's interest. Again, as in the case of dependent group contingencies, it is important to be careful when applying this technique. Children whose behavior is affected neurologically should not be put in a position as to affect rewards or non-rewards for the whole class, without adapting expectations to levels reasonable for the child's skills.

These group methods have been shown to enhance prosocial (i.e., socially adaptive) behavior as peers encourage, help, and provide support. However, they may also create situations where some children may threaten, punish, or coerce other children in the group. To avoid these problems, the teacher should be sure that the expected levels of achievement can be attained by all. Substance-exposed or ADD/ADHD children benefit from cooperative discipline and learning but should not be singled out in group contingencies.

Social Reinforcers

Children should be taught how to prompt others and provide praise and other social reinforcers as part of group methods. Social reinforcers are events or actions between two or more people that serve to reinforce desired behaviors. You may wonder if a child can be taught to provide praise and other social reinforcers to a peer. The answer is yes. Children can be taught social reinforcement techniques, such as making positive comments, writing congratulatory notes, giving "high five's," or dispensing stickers to each other as rewards. Even children with attention problems can be taught to be dispensers of reinforcement to others.

The application of group contingencies is most useful in cases where concern exists over academic underachievement due to mild disruptive behavior. Children who tend to exhibit aggressiveness also may decrease such behavior in the presence of social and group contingencies.

Although you may not have realized it, you use social reinforcers frequently in your classroom, such as saying "great job," "I like your effort," etc. Social reinforcers are generally effective, but you can make them even more useful for a substance-exposed child by providing detailed and specific feedback to the child. Instead of saying, "Great job," you can say, "You did a great job of paying attention and staying with the group in reading class today," or instead of, "Great effort," say, "I could see it was hard for you to do that math assignment, but you made a great effort to get it finished." Both classroom experience and the research literature clearly indicate the use of social reinforcers can have dramatic effects on increasing desired behavior and reducing misbehavior. Further, social reinforcers are convenient because they can be given quickly, require minimal effort, and can be used with groups or individual children.

Another advantage of social reinforcers is that children do not get tired of them and stop responding. Properly used, social reinforcers can be a powerful tool in your repertoire of behavior management skills. Social reinforcers should be used in response to specific behaviors that the child shows, rather than a global comment about the child. For example, it is better to say, "Great job," in response to a child doing an assignment well than to say, "You are such a good girl." Young children often do not know specifically what it means to be a "good girl," but they can recognize that they have done a task well. You also should not use verbal comments that, on the surface, may seem reinforcing, but, in reality, have negative connotations. For example, saying something like, "You're a good student, but I'm disappointed in you because of this low math grade," implies that you are disappointed in the child as a person. A better way to respond to a child who did not perform as expected in this situation would be something like: "You have done well in math, but this assignment seemed to give you some trouble. Let's see what I can do to help you with these kinds of problems." This approach lets the child know that you value his performance in math, but that this one area gave him difficulty. There is no suggestion the child is being criticized personally, but that this particular situation was troublesome and you can work together to improve performance. You are giving a social reinforcer (praise for having done well in math) but noting there is one area that needs attention.

Therefore, even in situations where some correction or help is needed, there are opportunities to give social reinforcement for some positive behaviors of the child. Remember also that every child has positive qualities. The most important point about using social reinforcers is that they should focus on behavior, be given immediately and often, and be clearly linked to observable behavior. The use of sarcasm is to be avoided at all times. No child should ever be embarrassed or humiliated, but for a substance-exposed child, who may be both neurologically and emotionally fragile, insensitive comments can be especially devastating.

Working with Parents

Although the major focus of this book is managing behavior in the classroom on a daily basis, we must not forget the importance of involving parents as much as possible. Educational research indicates one of the best predictors of academic success for children is the degree to which their parents are involved in their schooling. In general, parents at all socioeconomic levels value education and view it as essential for their children's success in life. Further, they are interested in how learning occurs. Many situations may make it more difficult for parents to participate in school activities. They might feel unqualified to act in partnership with the school or to help their children academically because of their own negative experiences in school; they may be coping with personal circumstances and stressors that command their attention; they may be experiencing depression or other mental illness; and they might be trying to function in an environment, either their immediate family or neighborhood, where drug use or violence is common.

Parental drug abuse often interferes with the growth of normal attachment relationships between parent and child. There is a greater risk for violence, child abuse and neglect. Parents often do not have the qualities and knowledge to be an effective parent. Research indicates that drug-using mothers themselves often grew up in dysfunctional environments and often had poor relationships with their own parents. They lack internalized guidelines for appropriate behavior and have difficulty setting boundaries in their relationships with their own children. Their parenting is inconsistent and is often characterized by poor communication and lack of closeness. Drug-abusing parents generally have a great degree of chaos in their own lives and in their own upbringing. Many of these adults struggle with their addiction, trying to "stay clean" and feeling very guilty when they are unable to provide adequately for their children.

Thus, the dominant pattern for drug-abusing parents, which includes poverty, poor coping skills, violence, poor education, and inadequate support systems, is often in conflict with effective parenting. These families generally have very poor access to quality rehabilitation services for their addiction problems or mental health services for their other problems. They usually do not have the resources to leave the community in which they are embedded, but staying in their environment makes it difficult for them to stay clean because of the social network that exists. Most often, those who abuse drugs are surrounded by other members of the addiction community, making it easy to be pulled toward addressing the need for the drug, rather than the needs of the children. Clinical interviews with mothers in our study have revealed that drug-using women have strong feelings of inadequacy and, while they admit that their lives are out of control, they do not believe they can do anything to regain control. They also indicate a high level of depression and anxiety. They often reveal negative feelings about their parenting capabilities and their ability to control or influence their children. Nevertheless, they almost always remain interested in their children's academic process and are distressed by the feeling of powerlessness and inability to help their children because of their own skill deficits. Teachers who feel empowered are in a position to empower parents to actively participate in their children's education.

Teachers too often blame parents for their children's misbehavior. They take the approach that behavior is learned and that a child's misbehavior is obviously the fault of poor, inadequate, or indifferent parenting. The data from our study of children prenatally exposed to drugs contradict this assumption and document the relationship of behavior problems to prenatal exposure. However, involving parents under these circumstances requires even greater communication and cooperation between parent and teacher.

There are many difficulties in involving parents in school, and as a classroom teacher you are faced with the larger school climate dimensions of this issue. Some schools are very successful in communicating a sense of welcome and warmth to parents and create opportunities for parents to become critical members of the school community. Other schools are less inviting, and some go so far as to make parents feel unwelcome or blamed. Your efforts to involve parents in their child's education will be influenced by the larger school climate in which you work, and the parents' prior experiences in your school. Spending some time assessing how the school deals with parent involvement and how this may influence your own efforts can help you plan your own strategies to be more successful.

Obstacles Faced by Parents

- Lack of confidence as parents.

- Negative past experiences with professionals.

- Under- or overestimating their child's potential.

- Under- or overestimating what professional educators can do.

Obstacles Faced by Teachers

- Little experience or skill in working with parents.

- Anxiety or resistance to parent involvement.

- Taking an excessively authoritarian or "know-it-all" attitude.

- Unrealistic expectations (i.e., too much or too little) of parents.

- Failure to take parents' concerns seriously or to take action.

- Emphasizing child or family deficits, rather than focusing on their strengths.

Actions by Teachers to Reduce Obstacles

- Recognize parents' assets and potential contributions.

- Recognize parents' role as "experts" in their child's behavior by verbal comments.

- Avoid patronizing, generalizing, and stereotyping.

- Accept the possibility that children do behave differently in different settings.

- Avoid putting pressure on parents and LISTEN to them.

- Encourage parents to ask questions and even to challenge you on specific points.

- Provide information about options the parents might explore.

Involving Parents in the Schooling Process

At NAFARE, we understand that you are a busy teacher and do not have time to have personal conversations with every parent on a weekly basis. However, there are some things you can do to involve parents that may help to prevent the development or recurrence of problem behaviors. It is important to note that addicted parents often need to learn to take care of themselves before they are able to effectively care for their children. Drug-abusing parents may not recognize your efforts to communicate with them. It is important not to feel defeated and give up even if you believe that your attempts at communication have been rebuffed. We often do not realize the impact we have on others.

The single most important thing you can do is to maintain communication with the home, even though it may be difficult at times. Following are some suggestions to consider in addition to the usual parent-teacher conferences.

Involving Parents

- *Try to call every parent during the first month of school to introduce yourself or send a letter home letting parents know when and where they can reach you.*

- *Develop home-school communication notes about a specific child's progress and send them home on a regular basis, as well as when a particular success occurs for the child. It is important to emphasize the child's progress, and not necessarily as compared with the rest of the class.*

(continued on next page...)

- *Emphasize progress from one point to another. No matter how small it might seem, it probably is not small progress for the child.*

- *As a class activity, perhaps a simply-designed newsletter could be developed with news about what the children are doing. To the extent possible, the children could work in groups to produce this newsletter, which should create positive effects on behavior. It would be important to ensure that all children participate on approximately an equal level and/or are included individually or collectively in the newsletter during the year.*

- *Send home notes with a child to inform parents about special events, projects, or achievements of the class.*

- *Communicate with parents about the importance of completing homework and thank them for their role in homework completion.*

- *Encourage parents to talk with you when they have concerns or questions.*

- *Ask for assistance or input from parents regarding the partnership process. It is equally as important to ask them for assistance for positive events, such as class parties, as for negative situations, such as disciplinary matters.*

Resist the tendency to predetermine that the parent cannot or will not help. Even though the parent might not be able to participate, being asked to help with a positive situation helps to enhance communication and creates a more favorable impression of you. It is prudent to think about what you might ask because asking parents to do something that is not within their ability can lead to their embarrassment and cause them to detach themselves further from school personnel.

When Problems Arise

Undoubtedly, there will be times when a teacher needs to contact parents about an academic or behavioral problem. Often, parents observe (or complain) that the only time they hear from teachers apart from established parent-teacher meetings is when there is a problem. By developing and maintaining communication on a regular basis, it will be easier to work with parents when problems occur. When you must contact a parent about a behavior problem, the following steps are suggested:

Contacting Parents about Behavior Problems

- *Introduce yourself and give some positive comments about the child, even though the immediate problems command your attention. These comments can focus on effort, attitude, specific talents, progress, or other points. If you have been successful in maintaining contact with the parents prior to this contact, they are likely to be in a much more collaborative mode and will receive your concerns more readily.*

- *When beginning to discuss the problems, it is important to emphasize the behaviors that concern you, rather than implying that the child is the problem. Describe the behaviors in terms of how often they occur, how long they last at a time, or how intense or disruptive they are. It is important to be objective and to have data and examples to help make clear the basis for your concerns.*

- *Discuss what you have tried thus far, and how much effect each technique has had. Then, say that you see the situation as a problem to be solved and that you would like to enlist parental help in arriving at a solution.*

- *Offer to meet with the parents at their convenience or at a time that is mutually agreeable. Since some parents feel uncomfortable in a school setting it might be beneficial to have the meeting at a neutral site away from school.*

- *At the meeting, restate positive comments, and again express your concerns about the child's behavior. It is not uncommon for parents to respond with, "He doesn't do that at home." You should accept this type of statement as truth or at least the parents' perception of the truth. Research and clinical experience have shown that children do behave differently in different settings, indicating that particular circumstances can have positive and negative effects on behavior.*

Let us assume you need to contact a parent about Ben's unprovoked aggressiveness toward other children. You have established communication with the parent and enjoy a reasonably good rapport. You call Ben's mother.

■ **Scenario - Ben**

"Mrs. Evans, this is Mrs. Reynolds, Ben's teacher. It's good to talk with you again. Ben is continuing to work hard on (a subject, project, etc.) and is making good progress in (a subject, task). (Here you should add some other positive comments. If this is difficult to do spontaneously, then you should rehearse some things to say before you make the contact.) However, lately (give a time frame), Ben has been having some problems with some of the other children. I have tried talking with him and the other children involved, but there doesn't seem to be a consistent pattern. I have reminded all the children about the rules against fighting at school. I have tried altering groups and reminded Ben of his assignments when I think he may be getting restless. We have a buddy system where we pair up children with other students, which often helps reduce problems. I have tried some other things that I would like to share with you, but so far, nothing has worked. "I thought perhaps if we could meet in the next few days, we could work on this problem together. You have knowledge of Ben that I'm sure I would find helpful in the classroom. I'd like to say again that Ben is (list some strengths, progress, etc.) and I see this as a specific problem that can be solved if we work together. Would you like to meet for a cup of coffee so we can talk about this? When would be a good time?"

Discussion - Scenario - Ben

Although this example certainly does not capture all the discussion and issues that can occur during such an initial contact, it points out some general principles of how to approach the situation to develop a collaborative, problem-solving relationship. An approach like this is much more likely to diffuse resistance and reflects NAFARE's philosophy that the child is not the problem. It is his or her inappropriate behavior at school that is the problem.

Conclusion

In this section, we have discussed some concepts and terminology that will help you to understand the nature of children's behavior, particularly with relevance to prenatally exposed children. By understanding these concepts, we hope you will better be prepared to address problems when they arise. The majority of this chapter has emphasized analysis of the classroom environment and various instructional and group interventions that may reduce or eliminate most of the problems. We also have emphasized prevention of behavioral problems, as there is evidence that effective management of the classroom can prevent up to 75% of problems. There will be times, however, when a child's behavior is so severe, disruptive, or chronic that these techniques are not appropriate or effective. Patterns such as extreme withdrawal, depression, and aggressiveness may warrant referral to the school social worker, psychologist or external professional. When behavior presents a danger to the child or others or causes severe problems, referral is appropriate.

Again, you are not expected to be a therapist or counselor, so do not hesitate to refer when necessary. However, remember that, although others may provide some psychological services to the child or family, you will still have the child in the classroom. Even if the child is hospitalized for a few days or weeks, his return to the classroom is highly probable, and some problems may remain. With increased knowledge, you will better be able to integrate the child into the classroom more effectively. You may, however, still need to develop some specific interventions for the child. In the next section, you will find information about how to intervene with individual children, using a logical, sequential problem-solving process.

TOWARD ONE ON ONE: INDIVIDUAL BEHAVIOR INTERVENTIONS

The first section of this book covered fundamental information about how prenatal exposure to drugs and alcohol can affect the child, and the second section described strategies you can use to enhance your students' behavior through structuring your classroom and through evaluating behaviors and the motivations for the behaviors.

In this section we will evaluate behavior further and examine some criteria for applying more individualized intervention strategies. We will then present a structured problem-solving process and demonstrate the process through a complete case analysis. Finally, we will describe specific strategies for one-on-one intervention and show how these strategies can impact the behaviors presented in Sections I and II.

Before We Start: Examining Teaching Styles and Preferences

When thinking about individual and classroom interventions as a teacher, you must start by examining your own style and preferences. Are you quiet and soft-spoken or dramatic and loud? Do you need organization and planning or do you enjoy the flexibility and spontaneity of "going with the flow"? Are you a director or a facilitator? Do you like to joke and play around with the children, or do you feel more comfortable in a formal, businesslike atmosphere? Teachers who prefer to work primarily with classroom instruction and are not interested in participating in student socialization are probably not well-suited for working with younger children, especially with at-risk populations.

On the other hand, teachers who enjoy working with younger children and are willing to invest significantly in socialization as well as instruction will be especially effective with the drug-exposed child in the primary grades. Teachers who are committed to addressing the special needs of drug-exposed children will have the opportunity to cultivate relationships that go beyond those necessary for purely instructional purposes. If, as a teacher, you are willing to make this investment, you can have a great effect on students. You are in a position to see a child every day under a variety of conditions and thus can develop an understanding of the whole child within his ecology. You are in a position to take direct action to help a child develop internal self-regulation strategies. You can develop contingencies and logical consequences for targeted behaviors and thus help the child move toward the development of prosocial behavior. Finally, you, the teacher, in your daily interaction with the child, can restore confidence and self-respect to the child who has experienced failure and neglect.

A second important consideration is attitude. It is important that you spend some time thinking about your own personal beliefs. Are you a teacher who is angered by the problem students in your classroom and frequently gets into power struggles with them? Do you see classroom management as discipline? Do you tend to overreact to provocative behavior and become threatened when your authority is challenged? Are you irritated by noise in your classroom? Have you taken the approach of, "If you don't bother me, I won't bother you"? Or do you view yourself primarily as a friend and facilitator to your students only to find they still do not act in a responsible manner? Do you often feel your students are taking advantage of you? Do you struggle to put out fires and find yourself ignoring or not noticing problems because you feel too overwhelmed and depressed to deal with them? Do you have trouble finding things and keeping up with the paperwork? Do you place classroom problems immediately in the hands of administrators rather than trying to solve them yourself? Do you emphasize control and punishment rather than management and teaching?

As you think about intervention strategies for the classroom and for the individual child, you should begin by reflecting on your own personal style and preferences. How does the philosophy presented in this manual correspond to your own perspective and beliefs? Understanding who you are as a teacher and what types of strategies you are comfortable with will optimize the potential for an effective and successful learning environment. Remember, research tells us that what a teacher does day in and day out has the greatest effect on what at-risk children learn. You, the teacher, can make the difference between those children who are able to beat the odds and those who are overwhelmed by them.

Understanding Behavioral Concepts

Two traditional tools widely used and researched by behavioral psychologists for learning and behavior change are reinforcement and punishment. You probably are at least somewhat familiar with these ideas and use variations of them daily. As we discuss our approach to behavior management, you will recognize variations on these two strategies that we have found to be the most successful in working with the drug-exposed child. We know you have your own teaching style and each child in your classroom has her own learning style. You will need to evaluate the special circumstances of your classroom and make determinations about the most effective use of the strategies we present.

What Is Reinforcement?

Reinforcement and punishment can be thought of as two ends of the same stick. On one end is reinforcement, which seeks to affect behavior and learning by *increasing* a desired behavior or behavioral response so it is more likely to occur. Like reinforcing wood or concrete to make it more durable and more resistant to change, so behavioral reinforcement strengthens the targeted behavior. Reinforcement takes place when an object the child likes (such as a novelty sticker or verbal praise) increases the frequency of an appropriate behavior (such as completing an assigned task). When the appropriate behavior occurs, it must be followed by the reinforcer (sticker, praise). If the behavior (completing the task) increases in frequency or duration after the reinforcer is given, then reinforcement has occurred. Reinforcers include everything from material items to privileges, attention, praise, power, and choices.

■ *Reinforcement always implies that we are trying to increase an appropriate behavior*

What Is Punishment?

In contrast to reinforcement, and on the other end of the stick, is punishment, which seeks to *decrease* the occurence of an inappropriate or undesirable behavior. In a case in which a child is making noises, the teacher may reprimand her in an attempt to stop or decrease the behavior. If the child stops making noises after the reprimand (or makes the noise less frquently) then the reprimand is an effective punishment. Time outs, verbal reprimands, and extra homework are all examples of punishment.

As noted in Section 1 of this book, our studies have found that punishment often does not provide an effective intervention with the drug-exposed child. This is likely due to the high anxiety levels often present in drug exposed children and the fact that punishment increases tension and anxiety, which can often escalate the undesired behavior. For example, John was making tapping noises with his pencil in class and ignored the teacher's requests that he stop. He was sent to timeout, where his behavior actually got worse because he became increasingly agitated and disruptive, struggling to manage the increased tension.

 Points to Ponder

Time out can be an effective interevention for reducing unwanted behavior by helping children calm down and not receive attention for undesired behavior. For drug-exposed children, however, time out often elevates the arousal level, making or more difficult for the child to calm down and reorganize his behavior. John was having difficulty with an assignment and was using his pencil to count. He became completely frustrated at this point and was unable to respond to his teacher's repeated verbal requests to stop tapping his pencil. When placed in time out his increasing frustration and anxiety escalated his loss of control.

■ *Punishment always means we are trying to decrease an undesirable behavior; however, punishment can actually increase such behaviors in the drug-exposed child.*

Positive and Negative Reinforcement/Punishment

There are two broad classes of interventions utilizing the reinforcement/punishment model: positive reinforcement/positive punishment and negative reinforcement/negative punishment. In this model, *positive* means the act of providing something in response to a behavior, either a reinforcer (sticker) or punishment (extra homework), while *negative* means removing something.

Positive reinforcement

Positive reinforcement occurs when an event or object the child likes (the reinforcer) is given following an appropriate behavior, which should cause an increase in frequency.

> *Jamal and his teacher are at odds. Jamal complains that his teacher is always picking on him, and the teacher complains that Jamal is constantly out of his seat, disturbing others and rarely completing his assignments without continual prompting. Jamal is interested in his baseball card collection. The teacher and Jamal's mother work out a system in which Jamal earns points for every assignment he turns in on time. The points are turned in to his mother, who exchanges them for money he can use to purchase baseball cards. Jamal completes his papers on time.*

Positive reinforcement has occurred because the frequency of the appropriate behavior has increased in response to the *presence* of the reinforcer.

Negative reinforcement

Negative reinforcement occurs when an event or object the child dislikes is removed after the child shows the appropriate behavior.

> *Tom fails to complete assignments independently that he is capable of doing. The teacher stands near his desk, prompting him to complete the work. John does not like the teacher's frequent prompts, and he begins completing his work. In turn, the teacher leaves him alone, and he continues to work to avoid future prompting.*

Negative reinforcement has occurred because the frequency of the appropriate behavior *increased* in response to the unwanted prompt's *removal*.

Positive punishment

Positive punishment occurs when a disliked event or object is introduced to the child to reduce an inappropriate behavior.

> *Eric is playing around and not listening to the coach during practice. The coach tells him to do 50 push-ups because of his inappropriate behavior.*

Positive punishment has occurred because the coach seeks to *decrease* the frequency of the behavior through the *presence* of the punishment.

Negative punishment

Negative punishment occurs when a desired event or object is removed, resulting in a decrease of unwanted behavior. Removing privileges, the most common use of negative punishment, can be effective for reducing misbehavior.

> *Tamara continually talks to her friends during class, despite frequent reminders to stop. The teacher punishes her by not allowing her to go outside during recess.*

Negative punishment has occurred because the teacher is attempting to *decrease* an undesirable behavior by *removing* a desired event or response.

 Thinking About It

Before we continue, let's take a moment to check our understanding of the concepts introduced so far. Read the following examples and use them to help identify your own preference and style of teaching.

Example: *1. Sylvia talks constantly, interrupting and parroting you.*

 Thinking About It

How would you handle this situation? Is your first impulse to punish Sylvia by taking away something she values, or would you seek to reward her for raising her hand every time she wants to speak? Do you tend to use reinforcers or punishment, and are they positive or negative?

Discussion

While each of these forms of intervention is effective, we suggest engaging Sylvia in a social problem-solving activity that would ask her to think about why talking out cannot be allowed in the classroom. Elicit her help in thinking about how you can help her better manage her impulsive behavior, providing her with some initial suggestions or pos-

sibilities, including positive reinforcement for not talking out or negative punishment (loss of privilege) if she does so more than a certain
number of times in a given class period.

*Example: 2. Keisha is noisy and disruptive in the hallway on her way to
computer class.*

 Thinking About It

How would you react in this situation? Would you punish Keisha by
keeping her out of computer class (negative punishment)? Or would
you establish a contract with Keisha in which she would agree that
every time she was able to negotiate a transition successfully (i.e.,
changing classes) she would earn points toward a desired activity (positive reinforcement.

Discussion
Keisha may become overly excited and overstimulated during transitions and thus have difficulty managing her behavior. You might be
able to help her develop better skills by discussing the upcoming transition before-hand, then walking with her and holding her hand until
she is calm enough to control herself effectively.

Example: 3. Keith makes fun of his classmate who stutters.

 Thinking About It

Would you take Keith aside to tell him his behavior is unacceptable and
send him to time out? Or would you reassign their seats next to each
other so Keith will get to know his classmate better and stop making
fun of him?

Discussion
We believe a teacher is responsible for the emotional and physical
well-being of all the students in her class. Non-negotiable rules that are
basic to the well-being of all children such as, "You will treat others as
you want them to treat you," (see Section 2) establish an ethical or
moral reference point to begin the search for different ways to act. In
this case, a basic rule of the class has been broken. Keith's behavior is

threatening the emotional well-being of one of his classmates. A strong and simple statement is warranted: " You will not make fun of another person in this classroom. Hurting others is never acceptable." The incident may allow for a class discussion about this rule and what is hurtful.

 Thinking About It

When you read through the examples of reinforcement and punishment, what were your responses? Which of the punishment or reinforcement strategies do you tend to use? How might you describe your style of behavior management?

As we move into this next section, we will be thinking about the concepts of behavior management in a slightly different way, encouraging the use of positive and negative reinforcement rather than punishment This approach is a result of our experiences in field testing behavior management strategies with drug-exposed children in classrooms across the country. We will focus on thinking about the messages students give us, and we will describe how to implement strategies that teach children to regulate their behavior themselves rather than relying on external limits and procedures.

Establishing Consequences of Behavior and Contingencies

When people speak of consequences of behavior, the implicit assumption is that these consequences are negative; however, the concept of "logical consequences" instills responsibility for choices and actions in children. While rules help guide children to construct their environment in a safe and orderly fashion, logical consequences allow children to internalize strategies of self-control and commitment.

In behavior management, any event that follows a behavior is a consequence, whether it is reinforcement or punishment. We have found the effects of punishment, especially positive punishment, to be unpredictable and often counterproductive when working with drug-exposed children, while the notion of logical consequences has been most effective. Teachers and children react positively to the implementation of logical consequences not because these consequences punish or reward, but because they help children look more closely at their behavior and think about the results of their choices.

Another key concept in behavior management is the contingency, or connection, between a stimulus (such as a positive reinforcement) and the appropriate behavior.

Receiving a positive reinforcement is contingent (dependent) upon the child's performing the appropriate behavior. Understanding this contingency relationship and the difference between a contingency and a consequence will be important when you develop interventions in your classroom. Children should not be given consequences unless they know what to expect and can make the choice to control their behavior appropriately. Then the consequence becomes a contingency because the child is put in the position of understanding the dependent relationship between his behavior and the reinforcement or punishment.

Jake is talking in class. The teacher tells him to stop. Jake continues to talk. The teacher again says, "Stop talking." Jake ignores the teacher's request. Finally, the teacher says, "I've had enough; out of here!" The teacher sends Jake to the main office for punishment.

Discussion

The teacher's reaction to Jake's talking is a consequence of his behavior, not a contingency. Had she said the first time, "Jake, if you continue to talk you will be asked to leave the room," she would have set up the contingency and given Jake a chance to make a choice and take responsibility for his own behavior. If you use a consequence without setting it up as a contingency, you lose the power of the contingency because you have not allowed the child to make the choice of what he will do. Establishing contingencies is especially important for drug-exposed children because it empowers them to make choices about, and thus learn to regulate, their own behavior.

The Problem-Solving Process

In the previous section — Classroom Interventions — we suggested that you consider easily remedied factors at the classroom level that might be the basis of a problem.

However, when classroom interventions are ineffective, you will need a more structured and systematic approach. Using the problem-solving process helps you to maintain an objective, systematic method for determining which interventions are most appropriate for your specific circumstances. The problem-solving process approaches behavior management issues as problems to be solved in a systematic series of steps. It involves the process of monitoring the child's behavior, adapting interventions to the individual style and needs of both you and the child, evaluating the success or failure of your efforts and then revising them accordingly. Each of these topics will be discussed as a step in the problem-solving process.

In the following discussion we will first describe the eight steps of the problem-solving approach. Then we will present a case study in which we will apply our problem-solving approach. Finally, we will provide a number of ways to apply the process to the kinds of problems most often presented by drug-exposed children.

The Problem-Solving Approach

Step 1: Identify target behavior

Step 2: Collect baseline data

Step 3: Evaluate contributing factors

Step 4: Identify appropriate behavior to replace the target behavior

Step 5: Brainstorm possible interventions

Step 6: Communicate interventions to parents and children

Step 7: Implement selected interventions

Step 8: Evaluate and revise interventions

The Eight-Step Problem-Solving Approach

Step 1: Identifying Target Behavior

Often children present a range of behaviors that challenge teachers. It is the rare child who can be easily described by a couple of clearly defined behaviors. More common is the child who is experienced as "difficult about everything." Problems often include a combination of academic failure, inability to complete work, difficulty working independently and in groups, oppositional behavior, and bad temper. Such a child is likely to be described as "difficult," "challenging," or "impossible," but often will be hard to describe in exact "observables." Thus, the first step in our problem-solving approach is to identify the behavior you want to change. It is important to identify the target behavior specifically and in observable ways. There is no way to define interventions that will make a child less difficult or challenging, but we can talk about how to help a child be more compliant, be more able to complete his seat work, and not hit others when he is frustrated or angry.

■ *The target behavior should be the unwanted or inappropriate behavior that occurs repeatedly over a period of time.*

In a classroom there are frequent disruptions that are isolated in nature and can be dealt with on the spot. Sometimes the situation is very clear, such as when a student calls out a provocative remark or creates a disturbance and can be handled with a brief response such as, "Take it easy, Juan." However, when this type of behavior is repeated, it is likely to be identified as a target behavior.

 Thinking About It

Here are some ways to verify whether you have been specific enough in defining a target behavior:

1. Can you name the behavior and document how often it occurs or how long it continues?

2. Can you describe the behavior to colleagues or parents so they know exactly what you mean (e.g., "Does not finish independent seat work")? If someone asks you what you mean, it may indicate you are not yet specific enough. Even in this example, you might need to add, "Does not finish independent seat work in the allotted time."

3. Does the child understand what you are asking him to do?

4. If a colleague were to observe the child or behavior in question, would she agree about the behavior and its severity?

The specificity elicited by answering these kinds of questions will be critical as we continue through our problem-solving steps. You will find yourself getting "stuck" in the process if you have not carefully defined the specific behaviors that are problematic. If this happens, you may need to return to this first step to reclarify the specific behaviors or difficulties the child is presenting. If you have trouble specifying those behaviors, you might try sitting down with a colleague and having her ask you questions about the problems until they begin to take more specific form.

■ Case 1- Tawanda

You find Tawanda's behavior to be generally annoying. Among the things you find annoying is that Tawanda talks continually and is constantly interrupting you and her classmates.

 Thinking About It

What behavior do you want to target?

Discussion
You can't target "annoying" without specifying it more clearly. The target behavior has to be specific and observable, and it must occur repeatedly over a period of time. Based on the information above, you would target Tawanda's frequent talking and constant interruptions.

■ Case 2- Chris

You find yourself disciplining Chris much more outside the classroom than in. You believe Chris gets into mischief during transition times and free time more often than during self-contained classroom activities.

 Thinking About It

Since "mischief" is not a measurable behavior, how might you identify behaviors that reflect Chris' disciplinary problems?

Discussion
You would need to start noting exactly what Chris is doing that is problematic. Each time you discipline him, make mental note of what he's doing. Typical behaviors include a) "jostling" others around when he is in line, b)

not responding when he's asked to get ready to change activities, c) ignoring requests to "lower his voice" and "quiet down" and d) running around and having trouble settling down when arriving at a new location, such as the lunchroom or art class. The target behaviors would be the child getting excited and not calming down during transitions.

Step 2:   Collecting Baseline Data

Now that you have specified those behaviors you think you want to change or modify, you need to collect baseline data about them. The term "baseline" refers to initial levels of behavior before intervention; that is, you want to objectively see the extent of the behaviors you have identified as problematic. This process allows you to record behavior in an impartial manner and thus gives you an objective way of checking your subjective reactions. All adults have a wide range of attitudes and responses to certain situations. Teachers can be affected by any number of things, including the way a child looks, the child's family background, how much the child is liked, the child's personality and attitudes, and experiences with the child's parents. Baseline data answer the question, "Do I really see what I think I see?"

Collecting baseline data allows you to observe behaviors and determine their severity in the context of the classroom. In some cases, the behaviors may occur inconsistently or sporadically, making it difficult to determine the actual severity of the behavior. Often in this case you may see that the intervention should be immediate and will not require a long-term, individual problem-solving process. Once you have established that a behavior occurs with enough frequency to warrant a more elaborate intervention, you will need to establish the context in which the behavior occurs. Collecting "baseline" data is not only about the child's behavior, but also about what is happening in the classroom when the behavior occurs. The context and conditions in which the behavior occurs are critical to selecting a successful strategy.

Baseline data also may be useful for demonstrating to a parent that a problem exists. Nearly every teacher has had the experience of talking about a child's behavioral problem with parents who fail to recognize or believe there is a problem. In some situations school personnel will videotape a child's behavior and show it to parents to demonstrate its occurrence and severity. Although we do not advocate such measures, obtaining adequate baseline data helps to provide documentation and justification for intervention procedures.

From an evaluation perspective, determining the extent of a problem by collecting a baseline allows you to determine whether an intervention has had any effect. After you have implemented the chosen intervention strategy and given it a chance to have an impact on the child, you will want to recollect data on the behaviors targeted. If you collected good baseline data before you started, then you will be able to compare your before and after numbers and determine whether your interventions modified the targeted behaviors and, if so, by how much. This is valuable information to have for parents, administrators and the child.

How might you go about collecting baseline data on behavior? First, remember the specific behaviors you are interested in, then create a chart that lists those behaviors. Begin to observe the child carefully to get a sense about those behaviors you believe you want to target and to help you establish objective criteria.

Objective Criteria for Observing Targeted Behavior

• *Frequency*

• *Duration*

• *Rating*

• *Student work*

Frequency of Behavior

You can establish baseline frequency just by keeping track of how often the targeted inappropriate behavior occurs within a specific time period; for example, how often a child is off-task during a one-hour period of independent seat work. You can determine the frequency of a behavior by counting all the occurrences of the behavior during a selected time period (hour, day, or week), or by taking a sample during each of several different time periods. For example, rather than counting the total number of off-task occurrences for three consecutive one-hour periods, you could observe the child's behavior for two or three minutes at several different times. This method of sampling, if done well, will give a good approximation of the frequency of behavior without diverting too much of your time from other matters. When evaluating frequency of behavior be sure the behavior is not being caused by something unusual in the child's environment, such as an unexpected announcement over the public address system or a group of children leaving the classroom for a special event. You can use any convenient system to gather frequency data, such as putting tally marks on a sheet of paper where you have noted the targeted behaviors, using note cards, or any other method that you might improvise.

Duration of Behavior

Another way to establish baseline information is to assess how long a behavior lasts. Rather than counting the number of times a student is off-task, determine how long the child is off-task within a given period. If the child is off-task for three minutes out of five, then the duration of the inappropriate behavior is 60% for that period. You can take several samples to verify that off-task behavior is occurring during other time periods and under a variety of circumstances. Duration recording is useful when behaviors are more continuous than discrete, such as staring out the window or not doing independent seat work.

Ratings of Behavior

There are several standardized severity rating scales that can be used to rate a child on a range of discrete behaviors. The results represent the teacher's composite impression of a child's behavior over time. Most school psychologists are familiar with these scales. You can consult with your school's psychologist to determine what scales are available and might be useful to you.

Evaluation of Student Work

Depending on the nature of the targeted behavior, the child's current classroom performance also may be helpful in collecting baseline information. Records of the number of tasks or problems attempted, the number completed, and the accuracy (e.g., percent correct on each assignment) can provide you with effective baseline data upon which to base an intervention for a behavior that interferes with completion of academic work. Letter grades are not adequate because they tend to be subjective. In addition, grades are not sensitive enough to show short-term changes. The child may make progress, but this will not be reflected in a change of grade until the progress continues consistently over a long period of time. This is inadequate for purposes of evaluating the impact of your chosen intervention. For this reason, student work itself is a more useful source of baseline data.

The need to be objective when collecting these kinds of data is critical because behavior and the perception of its severity is always affected by an individual's subjective experience and expectations. What is considered disruptive or inappropriate in one classroom environment may be viewed very differently in another. Each teacher brings to her classroom her own tolerance level, expectations for children's behavior, and preferences for some types of children over others. There has been a tendency in the past to label drug-exposed children as "unteachable" or "uncontrollable," which clearly is not true. However, it is easy for perceptions to be confused with reality and for children, especially those from troubled families, to be blamed for problems that actually reflect skill deficits.

In addition to using the strategies discussed above to establish a baseline, you also need to establish when the behavior occurs in order to "contextualize" the observations. Think about the behaviors you've noted: When do they tend to occur (first thing in the morning, after recess, at the end of the day, right before lunch)? What tends to precipitate the targeted behavior (an interruption in the daily routine, another child getting into trouble, the teacher working with a small group of children)? Can you begin to predict when you will be most likely to see the targeted behavior and, if so, what is the context in which it occurs?

By understanding a behavior within the context of the environment, you may find that the classroom environment is actually contributing to the problem. Perhaps you notice that each time Johnny is off-task during independent seat work he is looking at the constantly moving butterfly mobile hanging nearby. Johnny may in fact be off-task because of a distraction in the classroom environment that was created by the teacher.

■ Case 1- Tawanda

You have decided to target Tawanda's talking behavior and interruptions. You hope to determine if these behaviors are the source of your irritation with her.

 Thinking About It

What would you do to determine that your belief is actually supported by fact and is not influenced by your own bias caused by your general feeling of annoyance with this child?

Discussion

Pure numerical data would help support or dispel your perception. Counting the frequency of Tawanda's interruptions (i.e., how many interruptions occur in various one-hour work periods) would provide an objective view of how often she interrupts discussions. To create a baseline of her talking behavior, you may decide to record the percentage of minutes she talks during various parts of the school day. It would be critical to include observations that tell you the circumstances and time of day this talking occurs.

> **Case 2- Chris**
>
> *Now that you have decided that the target behaviors include those that indicate Chris is overly excited and is having trouble calming down, you can set up a behavior log to determine what kind of behaviors are exhibited and at what times.*

 *Thinking About It*

How would you collect baseline information to support your intuition?

Establish a log that allows you to record Chris' behavior each time you have to discipline him. Note what activity is occurring at this moment and exactly what Chris is doing. You may also want to note what you did in response to his behavior and whether it had a positive impact. You should collect the data for at least a week.

Step 3: Evaluating Contributing Factors

The problem-solving process involves consideration of factors that may contribute to the inappropriate behaviors you have targeted. Contributing factors are either "proximal" — that is, those factors that have a direct and close relationship to current problems, or "distal" — those that indirectly contribute to current problems.

Proximal Factors

Proximal factors influence the child's behavior directly. Examples of proximal factors include developmental status, learning disabilities, skill deficits, medical problems, emotional or psychological problems, poor frustration tolerance, low tolerance for stimulation, the classroom environment, classroom events, and medications for medical or psychiatric problems.

Distal factors

Distal factors cannot be changed in the classroom and are usually historic. Examples include the socioeconomic status of the family, the parents' use of illegal drugs, or abuse of the child that occurred when she was a preschooler. While little or nothing can be done about these factors, they are an important part of understanding the function and meaning of the child's behavior.

Often proximal and distal factors come together and contribute to current behavioral problems, but you may be able to improve classroom behavior by modifying their effects. For example, suppose a child with emotional problems tends to withdraw when criticized. The child may have a history of being criticized at home and may have learned to withdraw as a way to cope with the criticism. The distal contributing factor is how the child has been treated, which you cannot change. However, the proximal contributing factor is how the child reacts to criticism. You can approach the child in such a way as to reduce his tendency to withdraw and increase his group participation.

The first step in evaluating contributing factors is to gather information from observations of the child in the classroom. At that point you would talk directly with the child and the family. Since you've collected baseline data, you may already have some ideas about when the problem behavior occurs, which will allow you to hypothesize about what is going on. Perhaps you've noticed that Johnny's off-task, disruptive talking occurs whenever you are talking to the class without any visual cues or stimulation. Perhaps this child has difficulty with auditory processing and needs visual information to help him stay on track. Or in tracking impulsive-aggressive behavior, you've noticed that Daniel acts out after he's been unable to successfully complete the work you've assigned, suggesting low tolerance for frustration is a key to his behavior. Tanya's behavior is fine during the morning, but in the afternoon she can't stop talking, constantly moves around and doesn't comply with limits. You notice this is less true on days when the weather is inclement and the children do not go outside for recess. You begin to notice Tanya is unable to settle down after recess or any special activity that is active and unstructured, and she has a general deficit with structuring or organizing herself in less structured situations.

If you have formulated a model for the target behavior, you will want to talk to the child and family about your observations and gain more information from them about your ideas. If you have not developed such a model, you will want to use a conversation with the family to gain more information so such a model can be established. For example, Denisha's behavior is highly variable. Some days she is able to manage herself well and does not display the targeted behavior at all. Other days she seems to start out unable to manage herself at all, and by the end of the day she is out of control. Your classroom environment is quite consistent and routine, and you have been unable to identify any precipitant within the school environment that could explain this variability. You want to explore what else may be a contributing factor with Denisha and her family.

Always approach the parent as a partner who will take an active part in the problem-solving process. Information you gain from parents regarding immediate factors in the child's life (parent's loss of job, illness, death, marital problems, changes in household composition) will help you put the child's behavior in context and allow you to choose a more informed solution to the problem. Parents should be informed of the problem in a nonjudgmental way: "I have some concerns about Denisha's behavior in the classroom and would like to work together with you to see if we can come up with a solution." Since a parent's first response to a problem may be to punish, it is important to emphasize punishment as a last resort and stress the need for confidence and positive expectations in the child. If you are looking for information from the parents, be clear about it. Explain your observations and ask if they have information that may increase your understanding of the problem. Parents should leave the conference not only with an understanding of what the problem is, but knowing what their role in the solution will be.

When talking to the child and family members it is important to ask questions in a nonjudgmental and respectful manner. During a group meeting, insist that the child be allowed to speak without interruption and point out that everyone will be given a chance to talk. Listen and ask questions, pointing out any discrepancies in different versions of a story. Keep in mind that this is an information-gathering process in which you are trying to establish motives behind the child's behavior. When talking to children privately let them know that everything they say will be kept confidential (unless it has to do with basic safety issues, such as neglect or abuse). Do not allow the child to evade responsibility for her own behavior or project it onto someone else. "He started it," is simply not an acceptable explanation. Remember our goal is to teach children to manage themselves; the first step in doing so is to acknowledge and accept responsibility for their own behavior. This more likely will occur if you present your concerns with a calm demeanor that indicates you are there to help and make things easier, rather than being upset, angry or accusatory.

In talking with parents remember that they may be embarrassed and defensive about their child's behavior, fearing that you blame them (or their child). Substance abuse in a family is an especially difficult issue to address, and if you are uncomfortable with the topic you will succeed only in making the family more defensive. As a teacher, it is not your job to diagnose addiction, but if you feel there is a risk that alcohol misuse or illicit drug use in the family is affecting the child's behavior or performance in the classroom, you should be prepared to provide treatment referrals to the family.

Going back to Denisha's highly variable behavior, you will want to explore whether the parents or child have noticed that she seems to have some good days and some more difficult ones, and see if they have any ideas about the contrast. You might learn that some nights Denisha doesn't sleep well, and that she can't manage herself the next day. Or you might find out that some mornings Denisha is on her own because of her mother's sporadic work schedule and is angry and overwhelmed by the situation. Or you may learn that Denisha's father is in and out of the home, and that when he is around there are incidents of domestic violence that upset Denisha. Knowledge of any of these home-based problems will help you understand the behavior you are seeing and begin to plan ways to help the student.

■ *The goal of evaluating contributing factors is to help you develop an intervention that takes into account the function and meaning of the behavior.*

Establish contributing factors

Once you have documented a behavior and established the context in which the behavior occurs, you can begin to think in terms of the function of the behavior and move to the next step in the problem-solving process.

■ Case 1- Tawanda

You have collected baseline data on the frequency of Tawanda's interruptions and the amount of time she spends talking at various points in the school day. You have recorded a range of observations about the situations in which these behaviors occur.

 Thinking About It

What contributing factors might be influencing Tawanda's behavior?

Discussion

In evaluating the baseline data you can see that Tawanda talks more often during math class than other subject areas, disturbing the work of other children by trying to see their work or asking them questions. Interruptions, including Tawanda getting out of her seat, occur most frequently when you are working with another student and when, during a class discussion, you call on another student. A discussion with her mother indicates Tawanda most frequently interrupts her mother when she is on the telephone, putting her younger sibling to bed or is involved in some other important activity. Tawanda's talking increases during field trips, assembly programs and similar events in which there is a lot of activity and excitement.

■ Case 2- Chris

By collecting baseline data, you have been able to verify your perception that Chris has trouble managing himself whenever classroom structure is reduced, especially when in the hallways, moving through transitions, and when given more "do as you'd like" time. Under these circumstances, Chris becomes overly excited, exhibits poor self-control, and has trouble calming down.

 Points to Ponder

What are the contributing factors that may affect Chris' transition problems?

Chris' adoptive mother came in for the conference. She said he was drug-exposed during pregnancy. She confirmed his difficulty with transitions, saying he did not like changes of any sort and got "wild." As a child, changes in routine and being in situations that were highly stimulating were very difficult for Chris to manage. Chris' baseline information indicated that he was slow to change from one activity to another. (He was not ready for the new activity 50% of the time.) Chris also appeared to have difficulty when his "space" was invaded (in line, in the elevator during a field trip, during circle time). He became overexcited and noisy in the hallways and ignored requests to quiet down (70% of the time).

Step 4: Identifying Appropriate Behavior to Replace the Target Behavior

Most behavior serves a function for the child; thus, it is very difficult to eliminate the behavior or change it without providing the child with a substitute behavior that can serve the same function. This does not mean you cannot have clear rules about the unacceptability of certain behaviors. Some behaviors are simply not acceptable under any circumstance, and you should state these few prohibitions emphatically: "You may not hit another child," "You may not destroy other people's property," or "You may not put other people in danger." Such rules should be limited in number and stated in clear, unequivocal ways. Children often benefit from regular discussion of these guidelines, such as asking the class: "What are the important rules?" "Why do we have these rules?" Daily reminders and review are critical.

Because most behavior is functional, efforts to change it without substitution often are unsuccessful or only temporarily helpful. Let's discuss the function of some disruptive classroom behaviors and some possible substitutions for these behaviors.

Aggressive behavior is a normal response to frustration. Think about your own response when you feel very frustrated and you'd like to hit the first thing available. Think about the state of tension and stress you feel and the release you experience if you can take it out in some act of aggression (it's hoped that most of us have developed other ways of managing this state of tension). It often takes very little to overwhelm children with low tolerance for frustration, resulting in an aggressive behavioral response. Frustration can result when the child is asked to do something he doesn't want to do ("a demand"), including stopping an activity to transition to another. Schoolwork that is "too difficult," other children taking control, being teased, being punished — all of these situations can result in a state of tension to which the child responds through aggressive behavior. What can we offer the child as a substitute for aggression when the state of tension is too high? Remember, you can't make a child stop feeling angry, but you can substitute what constitutes angry behavior. In fact, just validating the feeling along with setting a limit can be a very powerful intervention. For example, you may say, "Derrick, I see that you are feeling very angry, but we cannot hit our friends." Feeling understood and validated often has a calming effect on children (and adults, too).

Some suggestions for the child to help manage his frustration include those that most adults use: relaxing the tension internally by removing oneself from the situation and "talking oneself down" to a calm state, using visualization to imagine a favorite haunt or activity, counting to 10, closing one's eyes, taking a deep breath and letting it out slowly, listening to calming music, or going alone to a place that is soothing. You can help children do these things when they are frustrated. You also can help them to reduce the impulsivity that usually accompanies these behaviors. For example, you may want to provide a punching pillow or stomping pad where a child can go when he wants to hurt another child by acting aggressively. By the time the child has left the situation to go to the stomping corner, he has controlled his impulse, and the stomping serves only to release the residual tension. Remember, relaxation is incompatible with arousal, so if you can help a child reduce arousal through relaxation, the other more disruptive behaviors that discharge the arousal state are no longer needed.

■ *The most important point in this step is to replace the function served by the inappropriate behavior with an alternative behavior than can serve the same function rather than focusing on replacing an inappropriate behavior with an appropriate one.*

Often people believe a child's behavior is an effort to "just get attention," as if this makes the behavior bad. All children need attention, some more than others, and some have learned the best way to get attention is through negative behavior. Sometimes these behaviors also may be an effort to gain control. While adults tend to feel manipulated by these behaviors, it is more helpful in the problem-solving process to realize the function of such manipulative, attention-seeking behaviors. What kinds of behaviors are you ready to provide attention to? How much control are you willing to give a child if she acts appropriately?

Once you figure out the function of a behavior, there are many tools at your disposal. You can look at the behavior in context and identify another behavior that is functionally the same but incompatible with the target behavior.

Thus, at this point in the process we need to think about:

1. Decreasing or eliminating the target behavior.

2. Identifying an appropriate behavior that is incompatible with the target behavior (i.e., relaxation is incompatible with arousal). Identifying the appropriate behavior is not particularly difficult, except that you must be specific and systematic.

Typical behavioral problems	Function	Substitutes
Defiance/Non-compliance	Control	Giving child control via choices and rewards
Talking too much	Discharge energy	Setting aside time for energy and energy expenditure
Can't settle down after recess	Can't calm down	Help child develop special routines and strategies that are calming (i.e. put head on desk then return to room, be alone for few minutes, extra preparation and time to make transition)
Defeated, frustrated, helpless	Protection against failure	Strategies for regaining self-confidence and coping with failure. Problem-solving strategies. Encouragement, praise
Hyperactive	Discharging stress	Very clear and specific behavioral expectations, contingencies and consequences. Cognitive strategies involving self-control
Shy, withdrawn	Fear, self consciousness in social situations	Praise and recognition. Responsibility, encourage peer contact and group participation.

■ Case 1- Tawanda

Given the results of analyzing the baseline data and contributing factors, you have developed the hypothesis that Tawanda talks most frequently when she is working on math, which is her most difficult subject area. Her interruptions occur when she gets excited or when attention is directed away from her. Thus, talking seems to be her way of responding to anxiety, excitement and lack of attention.

 Points to Ponder

Based on these ideas, what replacement behaviors might you consider?

Discussion

The replacement behavior would be to help Tawanda better manage her impulsive behavior, raise her hand when she wants to speak and wait for her turn. The replacement behavior for talking to peers during independent math or other work would be for Tawanda to give a cue to the teacher that she needs extra help or to pair her with another child for whom math is an area of strength.

■ Case 2- Chris

Chris' problems indicate difficulty with self-regulation.

 Points to Ponder

What function could Chris' noisy and disobedient behavior be serving?

Discussion

Since your suspicion regarding Chris' transition problems have been supported with baseline information and through your conference with his mother, you think he may be discharging excess tension and overstimulation created by transitions. He also seems to have difficulty

113

structuring his own behavior when there is not a clear, externally imposed structure. He then gets excited and has trouble calming down. Thus the behaviors that are problematic serve as Chris' best efforts to regulate and structure himself. You consider other ways Chris may be able to regulate himself, such as relaxation, developing a capacity to problem-solve and structure for himself, and learning calming strategies.

Step 5: Brainstorming Possible Interventions

Intervention Criteria

The list in the previous table (Function of Behavior) is a good example of the beginning of the brainstorming process. You have targeted the behavior and understand the function of the behavior. Now you need to generate a list of possible interventions based on the substitute behaviors you've considered in the previous step. However, in addition to thinking about the substitute behavior, you need to think about the logistics of implementing your strategy, what you would use to reinforce the successful use of the substitute behavior, and how you would set it up in your classroom environment. Thus, if you decide to set up a "calm-down" corner in your classroom that your students can use when they feel overwhelmed and unable to calm themselves, you would need to think about:

- Where you can set this up in your classroom.

- What resources you need (i.e., beanbag chair, cubicle, rug, etc.).

- How you would help the children use this environment when needed.

- How you would reinforce appropriate use of this intervention (i.e., a reward, points, praise).

- How you would explain this intervention to the rest of the class and to the school administrators.

In this step, remember:

- *Don't make any decisions at first; explore the positives and negatives of possible approaches.*

(continued on next page...)

- *Give each intervention serious consideration, evaluating it in detail.*

- *After the brainstorming and evaluation process, select the intervention you will attempt first. It should be the least intrusive one that makes the most sense.*

To determine which intervention you will select you should consider each of the following issues:

Criteria for possible interventions

- *potential for effectiveness*

- *acceptability of an intervention*

- *resistance and encouragement*

- *integrity of the intervention*

Potential for Efectiveness

The first question to be asked is whether the intervention fits both you and the child. Are you comfortable with the selected plan, and does it address your understanding of the function of the child's target behavior? Next, does the intervention take into consideration the complexities of the school and classroom environment? Obviously, each school has its own limitations and expectations, as well as structure. For your planned intervention to be effective, you need to be able to implement it within the constraints of your school and classroom environments. And finally, have you adequately followed the steps in the systematic problem-solving approach provided here, so that you know the baseline of the target behavior, the context in which it occurs and the function it serves? If you can answer these questions, your chosen intervention is much more likely to be effective. In addition, to be effective, the chosen intervention should be:

- developed specifically for the behaviors in question.

- appropriate for the situation.

- composed of the proper components.

- administered properly.

- given sufficient time to work (including time for any necessary modifications).

- powerful enough to initiate and maintain change over time.

Acceptability of an Intervention

There needs to be a consensus among all the players, (teacher, parent, child, school administration) that the intervention planned is acceptable. The teacher needs to be sure the intervention is compatible with her style, the child needs to "buy into" the plan, and the parents need to agree that a problem exists and that their child might benefit from this effort. When trying something new, you may find it helpful to ask others, especially experienced colleagues and the school's behavioral specialists, to think through your ideas and design with you. This is likely to increase your own sense that the planned intervention is a good idea that is acceptable to many.

Resistance and Encouragement

The first step toward effective problem solving is the commitment to making changes in yourself and your classroom. The easiest way to do this is to work with other teachers in the school to improve the classroom climate and your preparedness to deal with problem students effectively. Sometimes you will meet with resistance in the school as you find colleagues who have been beaten down by defeatist attitudes or have an authoritarian classroom management style. You may find the administration is resistant to change and feel frustrated that your efforts are futile. You may even have to overcome significant obstacles in yourself if you have an authoritarian approach to child rearing. You may have to battle your own tendencies for survival, your self-interest, and your anger and frustration as problem children test you on a daily basis.

As a teacher you face enormous pressures, and you often find yourself in a struggle to survive teaching today's children in a school without even basic support. We realize how difficult it often is to retain your faith in yourself and your children. However, when you believe in yourself and your role as a teacher, you will find the rewards — not only enhancing your own self-respect but earning the love and respect of the children — are enormous.

As you feel more empowered about your ability to manage classroom problems, you will greatly enhance both your own and your students' probability of success. When you feel empowered, you are more likely to seek alternatives, to anticipate the improvement or resolution of the problem, and to find and use interventions effectively. As an effective classroom manager and problem solver, you will gain confidence, you will stop magnifying problems, and you will become a better listener and observer of children. Your thinking about children will shift from attributing problems to causes over which you have little control to believing in your ability to empower children to take charge of their own learning and behavior. Your attitude will shift from discipline and punishment to problem solving and assistance.

Integrity of the Intervention

The intervention selected must be fully conceived, executable, and consistently implemented as planned. If you cannot follow through on the plan, then the integrity of the intervention will be significantly compromised, and it will be almost guaranteed to fail.

■ Case 1- Tawanda

You want Tawanda to raise her hand and wait her turn during classroom discussions and to ask for help appropriately when she needs it during independent work, especially math. If she were able to do these things, Tawanda would be exhibiting much better impulse control.

 Points to Ponder

What interventions would be appropriate to help Tawanda with her impulsive talking and interrupting?

Discussion

After explaining to Tawanda when it is appropriate to talk and when it isn't, you can tell her that each time she raises her hand and waits instead of interrupting, she will be given tokens she can collect to cash in for a treat or toy. You will remind her of this goal several times each day and acknowledge her when she raises her hand to help her know that attention will soon be directed her way if she can wait. Since math assignments create a lot of behavioral difficulties for Tawanda, you will check with her frequently to make sure she understands the work and is able to complete it independently. You will encourage her to raise her hand when she needs help. Additionally, you will recommend Tawanda for tutoring intervention in math. If she interrupts or disturbs her classmates, she will be isolated from them for a short "time out."

■ Case 2- Chris

You now have a model for thinking about Chris' behavior and have some goals to help him learn new ways of self-regulation that will be more adaptive for him.

 Points to Ponder

What interventions would be most effective in helping Chris navigate transitions?

Discussion

Chris appears to be typical of many drug-exposed children who have difficulty transitioning from one situation to another. After reading the section on transitions in Chapter Two, you realize that you have not been properly preparing the class for transitions, and while most children adjust to them smoothly, Chris cannot. You implement a classroom procedure in which you ring a small bell on your desk to indicate a transition is coming in 10 minutes. At five minutes you flash the lights. Because of Chris' difficulty, you give him the individual prompt of letting him know he must prepare for a change. During transitions you keep Chris close to you, putting a hand on his shoulder when you see him begin to lose control. You establish an "every other square" for the class to stand in when lining up so they are not too close to each other. You decide that when the class moves into unstructured time, you will spend a few minutes with Chris, planning what he would like to do with his time. You also want to implement strategies that will teach Chris how to manage himself internally with calming strategies including deep breathing, putting his head down or leaving an over-stimulating situation instead of relying on others to control him.

Step 6 : Communicating Interventions to Parents and Children

This aspect of an intervention is easy to overlook but is an important ingredient for a successful intervention. All interested parties ("stake-holders") need to be fully informed about the plan and given opportunities to contribute and ask questions. To be successful, the intervention must be acceptable to the child, thereby increasing the probability that the appropriate behavior will occur. The need for acceptability applies at a broader level as well: Is it acceptable to parents, other teachers, and the principal? If an intervention is acceptable to all involved parties, then its chances of being supported and successful increase greatly.

Interventions should be thought of as positive both in intent and effect. It is important that the child be included in the process of defining an intervention, since he will be responsible for executing it. In talking with the child you must be nonjudgmental and begin the conversation by asking questions to understand his feelings and to clarify your perceptions of the problem and its meaning/function. You must then lead the child to understand his role in creating the problem and give him opportunities to identify ideas and/or respond to a proposed solution. At this point both teacher and student will work together to set realistic goals and establish ways to evaluate progress.

Parents are an important part of any intervention effort. It is important to develop collaborative relationships with them early in the process. If you want parents to play a constructive role in the process, you need to remember that the goal is to find solutions to the problem, not someone to blame for it (review Step 3). Once you have developed a plan, invite the parents to a meeting where you can share your ideas and beliefs. Allow them opportunities to question your plan and add any ideas they may have. Create the final plan together, so all the stake-holders can participate and feel ownership in the efforts. Children should be included in at least part of the meeting with parents, so they see the mutual efforts and collaboration between home and school.

When parents leave, they should be invited to contact you about their child's progress, or you can arrange to send a note home letting them know how the intervention is going each Friday. That way they will know to ask for and expect such a report.

Communicate Interventions to Parents and Children

■ Case 1- Tawanda

Now that you've decided on an intervention for the target behaviors, you need to communicate your ideas and strategies to Tawanda and her mother.

 Points to Ponder

What would be important to point out in explaining the interventions to the parents and child?

Discussion

It is important that you communicate your concerns and intervention strategies to Tawanda and her parents in an objective and nonjudgmental manner, especially in light of the fact that Tawanda's behavior is irritating you. Tawanda should be told that, while you understand she is excited and wants to share her thoughts, her interruptions disturb both you and her classmates. You must allow Tawanda to help identify a meaningful reward. Tawanda's mother agrees to support the reward system at home. You agree to communicate on a weekly basis with Tawanda's mother in regard to her progress.

■ Case 2- Chris

You are now ready to communicate your ideas to Chris and his parents to allow them opportunities to respond to your ideas and "buy into" these new interventions.

 Points to Ponder

What would be important in your communication to Chris and his mother?

Discussion

It is important for the parents and child to know you believe the behavior is not willful. Chris should be led to understand that sometimes he loses control but that there are ways he can learn to get himself under control. His parents must be brought in so they can join in the process of teaching Chris to manage his own behavior more effectively. Staff members and administrators should be educated as to what regulatory problems are and how they should deal with them.

Step 7: Implementing Selected Interventions

Implementing the intervention requires planning. By this point you have identified the specific approach you will use, established the logical consequences or reinforcement to be used, and decided how and when to deliver them. Before you begin implementing the intervention you may want to think about the following:

- Do you have all the supplies you will need?

- When will you start?

- How will you evaluate your progress?

- Reiterate your plan to the child in simple, positive terms.

- Point out that you believe the child can be successful and that this plan will help things go better in school.

- Be sure to remind the child of what you expect of her.

- Be sure to remind the child of the reinforcement/consequence of her behavior.

- Provide an opportunity for questions. The child needs to feel like a partner in the process and understand how the two of you will work together.

After these preliminary steps, carry on the interventions as planned. As you implement your intervention there are some critical things you must remember:

1. *Don't deviate from your goals.* Remember, you have constructed a plan to address the most problematic behaviors. If there are some minor costs to developing the self-management capacity you are seeking, that may be OK for the short run because the real priority you've set will allow the child to make up the work later.

2. *Keep your eye on the prize for this child.* Remember, that may mean the child copies only half the sentences off the board or completes only half the math problems, but he does them carefully and accurately.

3. *Do not confuse consistency with rigidity.* You want the child to be successful because success breeds success, and chronic failure will ensure that your intervention also will fail. The child may need an extra reminder or chance to behave as desired. You may find that your initial plan is too difficult for the child, and you need to quickly lower your expectations so the child is successful. You can build back up to your original goals over time. Don't back yourself into a corner by declaring your plan as carved in stone. Give yourself some flexibility while remaining consistent in the execution of your stated plan.

4. *Use rewards as incentives.* Remember, rewards serve as incentives for all of us to exert the extra effort to do something that is genuinely difficult. They help build new capacities in children by having them exert this extra effort and discover they can manage themselves in ways they didn't know they could. However, for a reward (or punishment) to work, it has to be meaningful to the child. Some children will respond to verbal praise, others to stickers, others to treats and others to extra choices. Offering stickers to a child who couldn't care less about them will not give you the "payoff" you seek. The reward is not the intervention; it is a way to mark success.

5. *The name of the game is control .* It never feels good to be out of control, and this is true for children as well as adults. Children are frightened by the loss of control but often do not know how to avoid these experiences or regain control after an incident. There is a big built-in payoff to staying in control — it makes the child feel good.

6. *Be empathic.* Even as you set limits and manage behavior, you can empathize with a child's experience and emotional state. Thus, the child who is frustrated, angry, or overexcited will respond to the feeling that you understand him, even as you let him know his behavior (i.e., hitting, throwing, running around) is unacceptable. We cannot change the child's feeling, only the way he responds to the feeling. Couch your limit-setting language with empathy, "I see that you are feeling angry, but you

may not hit another child. When you calm down, let's talk about what to do when you feel angry."

7. *Be empowering; make sure the child experiences her own success.* Reminding the child, "I want you to have a good day because it makes you feel good and makes you happy," is critical. Reflecting this experience can help the child focus on her own internal rewards (i.e., "You must feel great about how well you did that!" Or "Isn't it great that another child picked you as her partner because of how well you've been doing").

The sequence of events becomes:

1. *The child does what you want her to do.*

2. *You provide a positive consequence.*

3. *You enhance her feelings of success, competence, and self-esteem.*

4. *This increases the likelihood of the child's maintaining the appropriate behavior.*

■ **Case 1- Tawanda**

You are now ready to start your new plan to reduce Tawanda's frequent talking and interruptions

 Points to Ponder

What do you need to prepare for implementation?

Discussion

There are no special supplies needed for Tawanda other than the tokens and rewards that you have selected for reinforcement. You are going to evaluate your progress through the same tools that you used in collecting baseline information. You will remind Tawanda each day of the plan, and talk with her toward the end of the day for a few minutes about her success or difficulty that day. You will remind her of the time-out corner and the circumstances under which she will be sent there.

> ### ■ Case 2- Chris
>
> *Chris' parents are very enthusiastic about your ideas and plan to adapt some of them to their own family situations. They also note that incentives often work with Chris to help him manage himself better. You decide to incorporate this into your plan.*

  Points to Ponder

Are you prepared to implement the selected interventions?

Discussion

Helping Chris learn to regulate his own behavior will require a change in the way you think about Chris and your teaching style. Rather than seeing him as disobedient and "naughty," you understand that his behavior may be just as distressing for him. Your teaching style will change from being controlling to teaching how to control. You have posted a set of rules and logical consequences that are positive. You go over the daily schedule each morning and preview tomorrow's schedule at the end of the day. You have purchased a bell for prompting the class on impending transitions. You have had a conference with colleagues to make them aware of Chris's regulatory problems, and they have agreed to reinforce your interventions when Chris is out of the classroom. You have set up a chart that allows you and Chris to monitor his success each day with special privileges being offered as an incentive.

Step 8: Evaluating and Revising Interventions

Give any intervention sufficient time to work, usually at least two weeks. Remember that the target behavior may increase at first; the child is testing to see if you will be consistent and stick with the plan. If the intervention continues without change for two weeks or longer, the behavior usually will subside to levels lower than it was before the intervention started. It is a rare occurrence when an intervention results in the target behavior, but if it does, you may want to make a change before the two-week period is up. Don't forget to remind the child of the plan each day or before each situation that is likely to create a problem.

If the intervention appears successful, evaluating it will not be a problem. Use the same technique you used to establish the baseline, and then compare the results. This comparison can help you explain to parents how the intervention is progressing. If the baseline happens to be in the form of task completion or accuracy, presenting the actual work in a straightforward format may result in the child or parents giving you reinforcement. However, if comparing the data does not indicate success:

1. You probably want to make some changes in the intervention. You cannot always predict how a child will react to a new intervention, and you may think of ways to improve your plan.

2. Return to the first step in the problem-solving process, whether you intend to choose a new intervention or to modify the existing one. Usually, as you review the early steps, you will identify the issues that require modification, thus making it easier to make appropriate changes.

3. Walk through the whole problem-solving process as before; repeat the process as many times as needed until you achieve success.

4. If a variety of attempts do not result in success, then you should seek consultation with another experienced professional. Consultation is also a good source of support to review interventions that are working effectively to decide when they need modification or to be phased out.

As you work to determine if your intervention has been successful, make sure you have kept your eyes on the prize in regard to the goals you initially set. If you change your own goals in midstream it is very difficult to gauge success.

After you've established the amount of progress the child has made, make sure you share information with the parents. Parents often are frustrated by the same things that you are, and hearing about their child's success can empower them to try different tactics at home. If your efforts have not been successful, then the parents are likely to feel less critical of their own parenting failures and may be interested in trying new things in collaboration with you.

Once the child has mastered the new behavior, you can begin to phase out the intervention, or replace the target behavior with another challenging behavior the child has not yet mastered. The intervention may be reduced so it is less intrusive, and rewards or incentives can be phased out. Children should first be encouraged to monitor themselves and determine if they are deserving of the reward. They should give themselves the reward for a job well done, rather than having it come from an external agent. Rewards can also be phased out by providing a surprise reward at some unexpected time if the child has done a good job continuing to manage himself. You can remind him that he needs to maintain the behavior to get a surprise, and then once every week or two, you can provide this kind of reinforcement. At this point the child has mastered the new skill and is probably experiencing self-reinforcing payoffs, such as competence, improved relationships, and feeling more in control.

■ **Case 1- Tawanda**

You have been implementing the intervention for a two-week period. You then spend three days recollecting data about the frequency of Tawanda's interruptions and the amount of time she spends talking and disturbing other children.

 Points to Ponder

After looking at your new data about Tawanda's progress, are there revisions you would make in the interventions?

Discussion

In looking at the evaluation collected over the past few days you feel you have had mixed success. Tawanda's talking has decreased slightly in math class and her math grades have improved. During the first two weeks of intervention she has raised her hand and waited 15 times and has collected enough tokens for two "free choice" period. Your efforts to isolate her in "time-out" have not been successful; in fact, she frequently sings or talks out from that location. You are not sure how the interventions are going at home because when you called Tawanda's mother at the scheduled time the phone was disconnected. You have written notes home but have had no response. You decide that there is enough progress to keep the intervention going, but you think certain areas need modification. You assign Tawanda a "study buddy" who will sit next to her and help her during math class. You take away "time-out" and substitute a reward system. After each class Tawanda does not interrupt she can collect papers or erase the board. You ask the truant officer to visit Tawanda's home to see if the family is still living at the same address and to ask the mother to call you or come to school.

■ Case 2- Chris

You have been doing all the things set out in your plan, and you've been talking through calming strategies with Chris when he seems close to losing control.

 Points to Ponder

How much progress could you expect to see in Chris during a two-week period?

Discussion

You are disappointed because there is little progress in Chris' ability to control the volume of his voice, and, while there is a slight improvement, he still does not transition from one activity to another very well. However, there is an immediate positive change in his "lining up" behavior. Although you have done your best to prepare Chris for transitions, the effect of your hard work is not as great as you had hoped. Teaching self-regulation and control is a long process. You should not expect to see any great changes in Chris' behavior in two weeks. The important thing is to be consistent and stick to the plan. The more times Chris is prompted and reminded of strategies that will help him stay under his threshold of stimulation, the more he will be able to use those strategies to regulate his behavior. Your success in managing Chris' problems in lining up leads you to believe you are on the right track in thinking he may have difficulty managing space. You think this may be a positive intervention for all the children and resolve to take steps to make group activities less "crowded."

Case Study 1 Violent Agressive Child: Juan

As an illustration of the problem-solving process at work, we will apply it to the case study of a child named Juan who is exhibiting violent aggressive behavior and has trouble keeping up in class.

> **■ Case Study 1 - Juan**
>
> *Juan is seven years old and in the second grade. He is imaginative, outgoing and active, but he is also easily frustrated, strong-willed, and sometimes very hard to manage. His teacher, Mr. Wilson, is concerned that Juan is having difficulty reading. Still, he is doing well in math. He is very slow to finish his work and does not follow directions. Mr. Wilson has observed that Juan gets angry very suddenly with no apparent provocation and recently has been exhibiting more impulsive behavior. Juan appears frustrated and often cries. Last week he slapped a girl during a verbal altercation. Mr. Wilson worries that Juan is having increasing difficulty keeping up with his classmates and that his impulsive aggressive behavior is escalating.*

Step 1: Identify the Target Behavior

Let's walk through the problem-solving process using this case and see what Mr. Wilson decides to do:

Mr. Wilson made the following list of all of his concerns regarding Juan:

1. slow work rate

2. inconsistent performance

3. lack of independent work habits

4. reading difficulty

5. frustrated easily

6. increasing impulsive, aggressive behavior

Remember: it is important to identify the target behavior specifically.

Mr. Wilson should be able to answer the following questions:

1. Can I name the behavior and figure out a way to document how often it occurs or how long it continues?

2. Can I describe the behavior to colleagues or parents so that they know exactly what I mean (e.g., out of seat)?

3. If a colleague were to observe the child or behavior in question, would there be agreement as to the behavior and its severity?

Mr. Wilson's list above was not yet adequate for purposes of specificity. He revised his descriptions to be more specific:

Original description	Specific description
Slow work rate	Completes only about one-third of spelling and reading work in the allotted time. Completes most math problems.
Inconsistent performance	Knows spelling words one day and forgets them the next.
Lacks independent work habits	During independent seat work, Juan is out of his seat, looking at other students' papers, and constantly seeking the attention of the teacher.
Reading difficulty	Halting oral reading. Cannot apply word attack skills independently. Is unable to answer questions regarding the reading beyond literal comprehension.
Frustrated easily	When given work that is challenging or told what to do, Juan becomes angry and upset, often screaming or throwing things or refusing to do the work.
Impulsive, angry behavior	Incidents of hitting other students, throwing things, getting into fights.

Mr. Wilson looked over his list of concerns and decided that, while Juan's academic problems were significant, his escalating behavioral difficulties were his greatest concern. He decided to concentrate on Juan's impulsive, aggressive behavior and target the child's way of responding to frustration.

Now that Mr. Wilson has identified the target behavior, let's make sure we can identify it specifically so we can think about collecting baseline data and contributing factors. Aggressive, impulsive behaviors have included: pushing a classmate when accidentally bumped, throwing a bat during gym, kicking his locker after coming in from recess and fighting before and after school. Juan's difficulties with frustration include: crying when he has to wait for his turn, crumpling up papers he cannot complete and throwing them on the floor, tipping over his desk when he cannot find the book he is looking for, and slamming a book down after struggling with a word he cannot decipher.

Step 2: Collecting Baseline Data

In order to collect data about Juan's impulsive, aggressive behavior, Mr. Wilson drew up a chart that allowed him to record the date, specific behavior, and any precipitating factors he could identify — including what Juan was working on at the time, who else was involved, and what time of day it was. Here is an example of portions of Mr. Wilson's baseline recording:

Date	Specific Behavior	Precipitating Factors	Observations
1/6/97	Threw his pencil at a classmate, hitting him in the eye.	Classmate refused to let Juan borrow his new crayons.	Juan had been reported earlier for misbehavior on bus. Classmate lent crayons to other student without problem.
1/7/97	Hit student on back on way to lunch.	Class had trouble lining up today and there had been jostling and physical contact during this time.	Classmate had bumped into Juan by accident. Juan was "squished" between two other students.

(continued on next page...)

Date	Specific Behavior	Precipitating Factors	Observations
1/10/97	Got into fight with other boy on playground.	Boy had called Juan names after Juan missed the ball in a game of kick-ball.	Juan seemed very hurt and angry by the boy's comments and responded very impulsively to the situation.
1/11/97	Threw crayon at another child.	Child was Juan's work partner on an art project and refused to do what Juan wanted him to do.	Voices got heated before throwing incident. Juan's request of the other child was not unreasonable.
1/11/97	Pushed a boy into a classmate's desk.	Juan reported the boy said something about his mother as he walked by.	This incident occurred almost immediately after Juan had returned from time out.
1/15/97	Swearing at bus driver.	Said bus driver called him a bad name.	Driver insisted that Juan not change seats. Stopped bus.

Mr. Wilson also collected data about Juan's problems with frustration tolerance. He again created a chart that allowed him to make some quick notes about these occurrences, including type of instruction or activity, a note of level of frustration (H=Out of control, C= Controlled but barely) and a notes column where he could record any behaviors and circumstances displayed in connection with Juan's low frustration tolerance.

Date	Specific Behavior/Level	Instruction/ Activity	Observations
1/6/97	Juan crumpled up a worksheet he had made good progress on (C).	Spelling worksheet on which he had to write sentences that included the spelling words.	Juan seemed to be working hard, but struggled on a couple of the items, quickly escalated and destroyed his work.

(continued on next page...)

Date	Specific Behavior/Level	Instruction/ Activity	Observations
1/9/97	Juan refused to put away his art project when told. Yelled at the teacher and then cried (C).	The end of art time. Class told to put away art things and take out reading book. (Oops, no warning given!)	Juan had not completed his project. He was working very hard on his project and seemed oblivious to anyone else in class.
1/11/97	Juan kicked over a chair at the reading table, stormed to his desk, put his head down and cried (H).	Juan's turn to read aloud. Teacher would not tell him the word until he tried to sound it out for himself.	Juan had been reading better than usual until the incident. He seemed to be using a lot of energy and focus before the incident.
1/12/97	Threw all the coats in the coatroom on the floor (H).	Juan could not find his coat.	A classmate had hidden Juan's coat.
1/23/97	Ran out of gym class (H).	Missed a shot intentionally. Threw ball out of bounds.	Gym teacher told him to "sit out."
1/24/97	Drew over his reading workbook pages (C).	Didn't know how to do the pages.	Juan couldn't decode the words.

After reviewing his charts, Mr. Wilson noticed some patterns he thought could help explain some of Juan's behavioral problems. He saw that Juan easily became frustrated and lost control.

Mr. Wilson contacted Juan's home to ask his mother to come in for a conference. When he was unable to reach her, he inquired about the situation. He learned that Juan's mother no longer had custody of her children, who were now in foster care in their grandmother's home.

Mr. Wilson called the grandmother, who noted that she was having problems with Juan at home and agreed to come to talk with Mr. Wilson the following week.

Step 3: Evaluating Contributing Factors

During the conference Juan's grandmother told Mr. Wilson that Juan's mother (Yolanda) used cocaine during her pregnancy with Juan, especially during the first trimester. She was 16 years old when he was born. He has three siblings. Maria is five, Mercedes is three, and Julio is not yet two. Until six months ago, Juan's mother lived alone with her children. Her major source of income was welfare. However, a Department of Children and Family Services investigator, following a tip, found she had relapsed and was using her income to buy drugs rather than provide for the children. She also was leaving the children home alone. DCFS removed the children from her home and arranged for foster care with the grandmother. The grandmother reported that the previous two years had been very chaotic for the children. She believed that Yolanda (the mother) had relapsed shortly after Julio was born, since it was about that time she started to be evasive about her activities and dropped out of her church group. During the past year she had cut herself off completely from her family and no longer saw any of her old friends. The grandmother suspected she was living with a drug dealer.

Near the end of first grade Juan was referred to the school counselor by his teacher. The school counselor reported that she had only been able to meet with Juan four times, as her counseling schedule was often canceled because of other pressing responsibilities. She believed Juan was misbehaving because of his family situation, although she said he was quiet during counseling sessions and did not volunteer much information about himself. When asked why he did some of the things he did, he always responded by saying, "I don't know."

Step 4: Identifying Appropriate Behavior to Replace the Target Behavior

Mr. Wilson now had developed some hypotheses about the nature of Juan's classroom problems. Juan had a low tolerance for frustration, possibly related to a variety of factors, including his prenatal exposure to cocaine, as well as his family problems. He was reacting aggressively and angrily when pushed beyond his limit for tension and arousal. Thus, the behaviors that were problematic served a function — to discharge the tension created by a range of situations, especially when he was academically challenged or frustrated, and when others refused his demands. He seemed to be especially stimulated by things that triggered emotional reactions. Mr. Wilson decided to substitute a behavior that was incompatible with the behavior Juan was exhibiting. Since Mr. Wilson could see on his charts that high levels of arousal led to problems, and he knew that relaxation was incompatible with arousal, he concluded that he could best help Juan by teaching him ways to relax his tension (calming strategies when he felt angry and frustrated), rather than reacting with violence and aggression.

Mr. Wilson made a list of calming strategies he could teach Juan:

1. *Breathing techniques.* Take deep breaths to relax, inhaling deeply and exhaling slowly through the mouth. Isolate different parts of the body that are tense and "send" breath to that area until relaxed. Think of a peaceful color and "blow" color through body.

2. *Visualization techniques.* Visualize something very peaceful and quiet.

3. *Self talk.* Keep cool, chill out, relax.

4. *Relaxation strategy.* Tighten body and then relax completely.

Other calming strategies for Juan that Mr. Wilson thought about were: counting to 10, taking a soft object to squeeze (beanbag, soft throw ball), listening to music, raising his hand to get help, putting his head down, and going to a quiet place to sit. He also thought he might find ways he could prompt Juan ("Settle down Juan," a hand on the shoulder) when he observed the child's frustration building, so Juan could become aware of his impending loss of control.

In looking at the charts he also saw that Juan often became frustrated when asked to do assignments he found difficult, as well as when he was interrupted in the middle of an activity, which occurred frequently because of his slow work rate. Mr. Wilson thought he might be able to prevent the frustration by breaking Juan's work down into smaller pieces and monitoring his progress frequently. Mr. Wilson also realized he did not warn Juan (and the class) when a transitional period was coming up (i.e., "You have 10 minutes to get finished before we go to music class"). Thus, Juan was not able to prepare himself for the transition. This, too, Mr. Wilson realized, needed to change.

Finally, Mr. Wilson recognized that Juan was having difficulty with oral reading. He consulted the district reading specialist, who told him that his "round robin" style of reading instruction was not very productive and effective, especially for children like Juan who encounter some reading problems. She suggested that Mr. Wilson read orally to the class and have children read short paragraphs in answer to guided questions. In regard to Juan, she made the following additional suggestions to Mr. Wilson:

1. Have Juan read silently before the whole group reads orally.

2. Try the "buddy system" of reading in which Juan and his friend read silently together and then answer teacher-written questions by finding the information and orally reading the passages containing it.

3. Use taped stories for Juan to follow as he reads silently.

4. Initiate a classroom procedure by which any child can "pass" when called upon to read orally.

Step 5: Brainstorming Possible Interventions

With some clear ideas about substitute behaviors, Mr. Wilson sat down to create possible intervention plans. To reduce frustration with academic work, he thought that after Juan completed each piece of work, he could cross it off on a check list and come to the teacher for a star. This would allow Mr. Wilson to monitor Juan's progress to help establish an appropriate skill level. At the same time, it would help Juan monitor his own progress and learn to ask for help before he became frustrated. After he collected a number of stars, Juan would receive a reward or special privilege.

Mr. Wilson wanted to help Juan calm down when he noticed early cues of frustration and tension and would try to catch him before he lost control by giving him some helpful words (put your head down for a minute, count to 10, squeeze your stress ball, turn your work over until you feel calm, do deep breathing, imagine you are a sailboat, etc.) and a touch on the shoulder. However, when Juan became out of control and displayed physical aggression, Mr. Wilson thought it would be most helpful for Juan to calm down and reduce his level of arousal. He thought he could set up a "chill-out corner" where Juan could go to do something relaxing to reduce overall tension. Mr. Wilson had had good experience using music to create a relaxing environment and thought this might be helpful to Juan, who could sit with headphones listening to classical music, maybe Vivaldi's *Four Seasons Concerto*, for 10 minutes. Later, Mr. Wilson would plan to sit down and discuss the incident with Juan, focusing on what kinds of calming strategies he might have used to manage his anger in a more positive way and what an appropriate consequence for his behavior might be.

His baseline chart indicated Juan had 20 incidents of frustration and/or aggressive behavior in a two-week period. Mr. Wilson thought it was reasonable to reduce the number of incidents during the first two weeks to 15, then in each two-week period thereafter to 10, 5, 4, 3, 2, 1 and 0. To help provide incentives and reduce impulsivity, as well as help monitor his own success, Juan would be rewarded with an appropriate number of stars — perhaps each star representing how many fewer incidents he had that week than the week before. Since Juan was very involved with his baseball card collection, Mr. Wilson thought that providing a baseball card of his choice for every 10 stars earned would be a good motivator, both for finishing his work and reducing incidents of aggression.

In addition, Mr. Wilson made mental notes for himself to give more time before transitions and to watch for Juan's needs for personal space, such as in lines or group work, on days when he seemed to be especially vulnerable.

Step 6: Communicating with the Parent/Child

Mr. Wilson once again called Juan's grandmother to ask her to come in to hear his plan. He requested that Juan be present at the conference. During the conference Mr. Wilson described his intervention plan and asked if there were questions. Juan and his grandmother both agreed to try the plan for a month and come back for another conference to discuss progress. Mr. Wilson promised to call the grandmother every Friday at 4 p.m. to discuss Juan's progress with her and let her know what rewards Juan had earned. Juan's grandmother agreed to encourage the same calming strategies and give Juan stars at home.

Juan indicated that he'd love to earn baseball cards, and that he also really liked magic cards. Juan also said he did not want Mr. Wilson to touch him when he came by his desk because it made him feel "mad" when somebody touched him. Instead, Mr. Wilson would just say, "Take it easy, Juan," as a cue. Finally, Juan said he got embarrassed when asked to read aloud because, "I don't know the words all that well."

Step 7: Implementing Selected Interventions

Mr. Wilson started his plan the following Monday. He had created a star chart for Juan and had a collection of soft balls and the materials needed to set up the "chill-out corner." He kept his original charts so he could compare Juan's current behavior with his previous behavior. On Monday morning he had a short conference with Juan, who reiterated his understanding of the plan. Mr. Wilson gave Juan a soft ball to keep in his desk. He pointed out the "chill-out corner," which was equipped with a soft beanbag chair, a set of headphones and a variety of classical music tapes. Since Juan loved music he had agreed that he would like to use the tapes and headphones for cooling off. Even though his music preference was not classical, he agreed he would give it a try. Mr. Wilson told Juan that when he was told to take it easy he should begin to use his cool-off strategies, which Mr. Wilson would remind him of at the time. He also reiterated the plan of reinforcement and consequences for his behavior. Juan asked such questions as, "What if someone starts something first?" Mr. Wilson answered by saying that Juan could always walk away and find the teacher, and that together they could figure out what to do. If Juan responded with aggression, then they would have to discuss the situation and consequences after Juan had calmed down.

Mr. Wilson also discussed with the class as a whole the chill-out corner and explained that when someone was out of control or hurting someone else in the room, it would be appropriate for that child to go to the corner until he was able to calm down and gain control.

Step 8: Evaluating and Revising Intervention

Let's take a look at Juan's progress.

Juan completed almost 70% of his assignments during the first two weeks. He won 15 stars and earned one set of baseball cards . His aggressive behavior diminished to 14 occurrences within the two-week period. However, when he did get out of control, the intensity of his aggression was higher. Because Juan seemed to calm down well in the chill-out corner, Mr. Wilson thought he would also encourage the child to use this strategy *before* an incident occurred, rather than only sending him there afterward. Mr. Wilson explained this new strategy to Juan, and they developed some cues to communicate about its use.

Mr. Wilson decided that Juan's progress was promising enough that he would continue with the intervention strategies he had selected. However, because of the intensity of Juan's anger in response to almost any social affront, Mr. Wilson decided to talk to the school counselor about hooking Juan up with an outside agency for additional services. He also asked that the counselor set up a meeting with Juan's grandmother to help her deal with the multiple problems of caring for her grandchildren, as well as to supply a referral to Juan's mother to social service agencies that could help her locate an appropriate drug treatment program.

Mr. Wilson also called Juan's grandmother personally to let her know about these plans. She said she had noticed that Juan lost his temper most often right after a visit with his mother, or when she failed to make a scheduled visit. Mr. Wilson asked that he be informed about the visitation schedule so he could monitor Juan more carefully immediately after a visit, which he thought might help further reduce aggressive incidents.

If Mr. Wilson had not seen this level of improvement, he would have returned to his list of target behaviors and reworked his plan to see what kinds of additional changes might be helpful.

Practicing Problem-Solving

This next section will give you an opportunity to practice the problem-solving process. Referring to previous sections and walking through the process with other teachers are helpful strategies. The following vignettes contain problems we have found to frequently occur in drug-exposed children. We will work through a series of focusing questions utilizing the problem-solving strategies described earlier.

Now Wait A Minute!

Are you saying to yourself, " Who do they think they are kidding? I have 30 kids in my classroom, and there is no way I can do all that stuff. I have lesson plans to write, behavioral objectives to deal with. With all the paperwork I have to do, I have no time left to even teach, let alone start a whole new thing. Anyway, I am sick and tired of all these new programs. Every year there's something new to do. That problem-solving stuff looks like a lot of work to me. Maybe if I had a special education class with only 10 kids I could do this, but in a regular classroom — no way!"

We are aware that the multiple roles you must fill as a teacher are often overwhelming. You are expected to be a nurse, a parent, a social worker, and a policeman, and you say to yourself, "Now they expect me to be a psychologist, too." We believe that what we propose will take no more time than you normally would spend on discipline. We believe that if, for every minute you spend disciplining now, you substitute one of our approaches, at the end of the day you will find you actually may have gained instructional time — not lost it. We believe that, by working through the problem-solving approach to behavior management, you will use your colleagues, the children themselves, the parents and administration as part of the solution. We believe that, if you bring others into the process, you will feel less isolated and more empowered about your ability to manage classroom problems, and you will greatly enhance your probability for success. We believe that you will be more likely to seek alternatives, to anticipate the resolution or improvement of the problem, and to find and use interventions correctly. We ask you to try, even though you may have misgivings, because as you find success in our approach you will feel much more confident in dealing with the challenging behaviors in your classroom.

As you go through this next section, we encourage you to use our case examples solely as jumping off points in this process. We ask that as you read each case example, you think about children that have presented similar behaviors and challenges in your classroom and think about the context in which the behaviors occur. These cases come from our work and research with drug-exposed children and represent some real life situations you will face in the classroom.

Case Study 2 Erratic Easily Overstimulated Child: John

■ **Case Study 2 - John**

John's birth mother used alcohol and cocaine throughout her pregnancy. He is described by his adoptive parents and teachers as a sweet, creative boy who gets over-stimulated very easily and loses control for no apparent reason. When John was small, his mother reported that he would "get wild" and throw toys without provocation. She also described times when he accidentally bit or hurt other children when engaged in "roughhousing." In school he doesn't settle down after recess. He has trouble using his "indoor voice" when engaged in physical activities. His mother describes him as "vibrating" in anticipation of exciting events such as birthday parties or holidays. He also is easily frustrated and becomes overly anxious when demands are placed on him, resulting in similar types of behaviors, which indicates he is overwhelmed and out of control.

All children get over-excited and somewhat out of control at times but when asked to calm down or stop screaming, they have the inner resources to bring the excitement level down enough to calm themselves. Drug-exposed children, however, often have regulatory problems and are unable to do that. Think about children who have regulatory problems. They run when they should be walking and when asked to stop they appear oblivious to your request. These children's voices are too loud and they do not respond when asked to quiet down. This type of child becomes so excited when watching the school talent show he appears to be "jumping out of his skin." He's the child you keep close to you when moving from one place to another and who must sit on your lap during story time. This child may also be very overstimulated by emotional experiences, and be susceptible to overwhelming anxiety when in difficult situations or when demands are placed on him. He may respond with a range of behaviors that you might describe as extreme. Finally, he not only has difficulty calming down when excited or overstimulated, but his behaviors actually tend to escalate once he gets going.

As we step through the problem-solving process, think not of John, but of the child you have identified in your mind.

Step 1: Identifying Target Behavior

Focusing Questions:

- What is the behavior I wish to change?

- Is the behavior specific and observable?

- Does the behavior occur repeatedly over time?

- Can I describe the behavior so others know exactly what I mean?

- Will the child understand what I want him to do?

- Do my colleagues agree the behavior is problematic?

- Can they confirm my perceptions on this?

Discussion:

When working with children who display these types of patterns, appropriate target behaviors vary considerably. If we were evaluating John, we would think about target behaviors such as failing to calm down when returning to the classroom after a special activity; becoming so excited during stimulating activities that he stops listening; becoming too loud (i.e., shouting, disrupting other children); and starting to intrude on another child's space. It may be appropriate to target behaviors that surface when the child is feeling anxious, especially when demands are placed on him. The hallmark pattern for these children is that situations that are stimulating or under-structured result in less behavioral control, and once control is lost it is difficult for the child to calm down. Instead his behaviors seem to escalate.

Step 2: Collecting Baseline Data

Focusing Questions:

- What form of charting will help me collect information on the target behavior?

- Is frequency and duration important information to have for baseline information?

- What would be the best way to collect information on the circumstancessurrounding the target behavior?

- Will collecting work samples be helpful in this case?

Discussion:

In general, the circumstances and context in which the behavioral problems arise are very important. While you need to document what exact behavior is requiring special attention, it will be characteristics of the situations that will tell you what you need to do to reduce the problems. You will also want to note the child's response to the different types of disciplinary responses you are currently using. What happens if you punish the child, place him in time-out or yell at him. Does he calm down, or does his behavior get even worse? Among the things to note as you keep track of target behaviors is whether the child seems to be responding primarily to environmental stimulation (lots of stuff going on) or to emotional stimulation, such as becoming overly excited when performing in a class skit at an assembly or anxiety about a test-taking situation. Because a child with regulatory problems generally has a low threshold for arousal, anything that potentially increases the arousal state above that mark can result in behavioral problems.

Step 3 : Evaluating Contributing Factors

Focusing Questions:

- What do I know about this child? Skill deficits? Learning/emotional problems?

- What influences cannot be changed?

- Have I asked the child to tell me about himself?

- What do I need to know about the family?

Focusing Questions:

- What questions can I ask the family?

- What is the context of the behavior?

- Have I specified the exact circumstances in which the target behaviors most often occur?

- Is my style of teaching, disciplining, or classroom environment a contributing factor?

Discussion:

Two major areas need to be explored to be able to reach sound conclusions about children with these kinds of problems: classroom/school environment and family information. You need to look carefully at the context in which the behavior occurs, looking at the level of structure and stimulation. You also need to think about how this child responds to different types of interventions you may provide. How does the child respond to punishment? Does the child tend to escalate? The other important thing to look at is the family members' experience with the child, and to what extent their observations are consistent with your own. While parents often do not have any idea how to understand their child's behavior, they are able to describe the patterns that you may be picking up on in school. Together you can make some reasonable guesses about the child's behavior patterns. However, if in your meeting with parents you sense that the home environment is extremely chaotic, that parents do not provide even basic structure for their child, and are unprepared to observe their behavior, then you may be looking at a child whose behavior reflects this history and environment. The child may never have learned how to modulate his feelings and regulate himself because his parents have never provided the opportunity and responses that allow children to develop these capacities.

Step 4: Identifying Appropriate Behavior to Replace the Target Behavior

Focusing Questions:

- What is the function of the behavior?

- What behavior can I substitute that will serve the same function?

Discussion:

As alluded to above, the behaviors most commonly seen in children with regulatory difficulties are functionally serving to discharge the stimulation and arousal that has created too much tension for the child. Thus, if you try to eliminate the behavior without addressing this function, you likely will see replacement behaviors emerge that are just as problematic as the ones you have tried to eliminate. Instead, you need to think in terms of alternate strategies the child can use to discharge the excess stimulation, as well as how to avoid becoming overwhelmed in the first place. To avoid over-arousal, you will need to teach the child to recognize when he is approaching loss of control. Initially, this may require verbal cueing from teachers and parents so the child can learn to identify this feeling. Then the child should be helped to take himself out of the situation or use calming strategies to avoid over-arousal. You also will need to provide actual instruction in calming strategies, such as how to go to a quiet place and chill out or how to close one's eyes, take deep breaths, count to 10, clench then relax the body, or how to use the stress ball the child keeps in his desk. Including in-centives to help the child use cognitive strategies to mediate between the impulse and the desired behavior (developing a new capacity) often can be helpful.

Step 5: Brainstorming Possible Interventions

Focusing Questions:

- Where can I set up the intervention in my classroom?

- Do I need special resources for this intervention?

- What type of reinforcement will I use?

- Have I explained the intervention to the class? The child? The school staff and administrator?

- Do I feel comfortable trying this intervention?

- Do the baseline data indicate the need for this intervention?

- Can the intervention produce the desired change?

- Is the intervention acceptable to the child? The parents?

Discussion:

Once you have developed your hypotheses about the function of the behavior and the circumstances in which it occurs and have developed some ideas about what might serve as replacement behaviors, you can sit down and specify exactly how you will implement your ideas. What incentives might work? What do you think would be least intrusive but powerful enough to create behavior change? It also is critical that you like and feel comfortable with the intervention you have planned so you are in a position to sell it to the other players involved. Do not try to do too many things at one time. Implement only a couple of strategies; you can add other components later.

Step 6: Communicating Interventions to Parents and Children

Focusing Questions:

- Have the parents been included in the process?

- Has the child been included in the process?

- Did you ask the parents and child if they have questions?

- Did you invite suggestions from the parents and child?

- Have you set up a follow-up plan of communication for the parents and child?

Discussion:

Many parents with a child who has regulatory problems do not recognize the patterns in their child's behavior and would benefit from having the information you can provide. They also can be very helpful by utilizing the same relaxation strategies at home, as well as recognizing and cueing their child when they see that he is becoming overwhelmed or overstimulated.

Step 7: Implementing Selected Interventions

Focusing Questions:

- Do I have all the supplies I need?

- Do I have a start/end date?

Focusing Questions:

- Do I have an evaluation plan?

- Have I communicated with the parents and child?

- Do I have a plan to remind the child daily what is expected   of him?

- Have I shown the child how to use these strategies when needed?

- Do I have a plan of consequences or reward for positive behavior?

- Have I allowed for questions and revisions with parents/ child?

- Am I keeping my eye on the goal?

- Am I as flexible as I need to be?

- Am I empathic with the child?

Discussion:

While the particulars may vary, the thing that is important to keep in mind with children with regulatory problems is that they need cues to help them recognize when they are at risk of losing control or becoming overstimulated. They also need help to learn and then use alternate self-regulation (calming) strategies, with frequent reminders and a great deal of positive reinforcement. Implementing logical consequences is also appropriate. The key is prevention: You must intervene before the child loses control, or you will not be effective. Many upfront reminders, frequent review, and continuing attention to the child when he is in a situation that may lead to problems are critical.

Step 8: Evaluating and Revising Interventions

Focusing Questions:

- Have I allowed enough time for the intervention to work?

- Have I created a system for comparing pre- and post-intervention?

- Have I called the parents to tell them how intervention is progressing?

- Have I kept the same goal from beginning to end?

Discussion:

It will take time for a child with regulatory problems to learn to monitor himself without prompting and help. However, your preventive interventions should be reducing the amount of discipline you are having to use with the child, as he begins to utilize the preventive strategies. If you look at post-intervention data that indicate you are having to discipline as frequently as before your intervention, then you need to take a careful look at how consistently you are reminding the child, adding incentives when he uses the strategies being coached, and step up the preventive end of your efforts in problematic situations. As with all cases, checking in with parents is important, especially if they are trying to use some of the same strategies at home. Reviewing progress with the child, focusing on how wonderful it must feel to be in control and not to have to be yelled at all the time, is also important. Over time, you will want to reduce how much prevention and cueing you provide, so the child begins to rely on his own regulatory capacities. This is the long-term goal ("keep your eye on the prize") and will take time, patience, and collaboration with other staff, especially the next classroom teacher the child will have.

Case Study 3 Oppositional Defiant Behavior: Katrina

■ Case Study 3 - Katrina

Katrina is an eight-year-old second-grader who seems to want to fight with you about everything. She often refuses to do what you say and is openly defiant and oppositional in her stance with authority. You have punished her for noncompliance, taking away recess, making her stay after school and sending her to the principal's office. All these efforts seem to be of no avail, and, if anything, seem to make the oppositionality worse with Katrina saying she "doesn't care." You have talked to her first-grade teacher, who also experienced some oppositional behavior but placed fewer demands on Katrina and saw less of the behavior she currently is exhibiting.

CA

 Thinking About It

Have you had experiences with children like Katrina? Think about those children as you work through the eight problem-solving steps.

Discussion

Patterns of oppositional-defiant behavior are frequently seen in drug-exposed children. While prenatal drug exposure seems to contribute to these patterns, so too do the other experiences the children have had with authority figures. Drug exposure may contribute to the patterns because these children experience demands as frustrating or overwhelming and feel "out of control." Often children will respond with a self-protective stance of refusal and oppositionality, which may help them feel more in control. Also, like aggression, defiance is a "natural" response to stress and feeling overwhelmed by the demands of others. (Has this ever happened to you?) In addition, inconsistent experiences with authority, not having experienced empathy from authority figures, overly punitive parenting styles and general lack of trust of authority can also contribute to these patterns. Children who have been moved from household to household, because of foster placements or because their parents utilize friends and family members as frequent surrogate parents without a clear routine, are also likely to display these behaviors. They often are an effort to regain some sense of control in a world in which the children feel very little control..

Step 1: Identifying Target Behavior

Focusing Questions:

- What is the behavior I wish to change?
- Is the behavior specific and observable?
- Does the behavior occur repeatedly over time?
- Can I describe the behavior so others know exactly what I mean?
- Will the child understand what I want him to do?
- Do my colleagues agree the behavior is problematic?
- Can they confirm my perceptions on this?

Discussion:

Clearly, the target behavior for these children is the oppositional behavior itself. Examples of oppositional behavior are refusal to comply with requests, angry responses when told to do something, and other noncompliant behaviors they may exhibit with peers, especially when in groups.

Step 2: Collecting Baseline Data

Focusing Questions:

- What form of charting will help me collect information on the target behavior?
- Is frequency and duration important information to have for baseline information?

Focusing Questions:

- What would be the best way to collect information on the circumstances surrounding the target behavior?

- Will collecting work samples be helpful in this case?

Discussion:

You will want to establish the frequency with which these types of children are oppositional in response to requests from authority and look for patterns that may give you clues about the circumstances promoting such behavior. You also may look at the other side and try to track the circumstances under which this child is compliant. How was the request made? What was it about? Was it made differently from the requests that resulted in defiance?

Step 3 : Evaluating Contributing Factors

Focusing Questions:

- What do I know about this child? Skill deficits? Learning/emotional problems?

- What are the influences that cannot be changed?

- Have I asked the child to tell me about himself?

- What do I need to know about the family?

- What questions can I ask the family?

- What is the context of the behavior? Have I specified the exact circumstances under which the target behaviors most often occur?

Focusing Questions:

- Is my style of teaching or disciplining or the classroom environment a contributing factor?

Discussion:

When you meet with the parents you will probably want to explore whether the child displays similarly oppositional behaviors at home and if the parents have found any ways of reducing this behavior. Chances are they feel as "stuck" as you do and may be overutilizing corporal punishment. You may want to talk with other teachers about their experiences and see if their approach with a given child has resulted in different behavior. You would probably want to find out something about the child's history as it pertains to these patterns.

Step 4: Identifying Appropriate Behavior to Replace the Target Behavior

Focusing Questions:

- What is the function of the behavior?

- What behavior can I substitute that will serve the same function?

Discussion:

Replacement behavior logically needs to move toward increased compliance with requests, less talking back, and more cooperation with teachers and peers. However, the only way to be successful in reaching this goal is to appreciate the child's need to control, to trust and to not feel threatened. Without taking into account these circumstances, the child's oppositionality is likely to increase.

Step 5: Brainstorming Possible Interventions

Focusing Questions:

- Where can I set up the intervention in my classroom?

- Do I need special resources for this intervention?

- What type of reinforcement will I use?

- Have I explained the intervention to the class? The child? The school staff and administrator?

- Do I feel comfortable trying this intervention?

- Do the baseline data indicate the need for this intervention?

- Can the intervention produce the desired change?

- Is the intervention acceptable to the child? The parents?

Discussion:

The key to intervening with oppositional behaviors is to circumvent the oppositionality by "putting the child in charge." A series of positive incentives that are meaningful to the child is often an effective way of doing this. If the child elects not to comply with the teacher's requests for work or behavior, she can choose to sit at her desk and do nothing. However, she will not receive the privileges established by the incentives. In addition, it is critical to be nonconfrontational and not to back yourself into a corner by saying things like, "You'll sit there until the work is done," because you cannot follow through on such threats. Set up the incentives so the child can be initially successful; this will build on itself so that over time the incentives can be reduced. Do not engage in power struggles; you almost always will lose. Pick your battles very carefully. Empathy and trust-building are other critical dimen-

Discussion:

sions of working with the this type of child. Gentle reminders of expectations, couched with words of empathy, may help the child relax and reduce oppositionality.

Step 6: Communicating Interventions to Parents and Children

Focusing Questions:

- Have the parents been included in the process?

- Has the child been included in the process?

- Did you ask the parents and child if they have questions?

- Did you invite suggestions from the parents and child?

- Have you set up a follow-up plan of communication for the parents and child?

Discussion:

Often parents are caught in the same patterns as teachers and are further contributing to the problems by punitive responses. You will need to help them read the behavior differently and maybe start using some new tactics at home. Both parents and child are critical in helping you identify meaningful incentives. The child needs to hear that you care about her and are looking for ways to make school a happier experience for her.

Step 7: Implementing Selected Interventions

Focusing Questions:

- Do I have all the supplies I need?

- Do I have a start/end date?

- Do I have an evaluation plan?

- Have I communicated with the parents and child?

- Do I have a plan to remind the child daily what is expected of him?

- Have I shown the child how to use these strategies when needed?

- Do I have a plan of consequences or reward for positive behavior?

- Have I allowed for questions and revisions with parent/child?

- Am I keeping my eye on the goal?

- Am I as flexible as I need to be?

- Am I empathic with the child?

Discussion:

You will need to work to change your stance with the child from one of controlling to one of giving the child the choice and control. It is critical that you stay very calm with the child so she stays calm and can make the right choice. You also need to offer lots of reminders, provide incentives consistently and set aside time to develop a positive relationship as part of the intervention process. She needs to feel that she is respected, that she is being treated fairly and that she is being heard.

Step 8 : Evaluating and Revising Interventions

Focusing Questions:

- Have I allowed enough time for the intervention to work?
- Have I created a system for comparing pre- and post-intervention?
- Have I called the parents to tell them how intervention is progressing?
- Have I kept the same goal from beginning to end?

Discussion:

Sometimes children don't trust the teacher so much that they challenge her intervention before ever giving it a chance, thus increasing the oppositional behavior. You may have a couple of bad days before the better ones start. While children are often reluctant to give up their oppositional position, over time you should see a modified stance as they feel less vulnerable and more in control. If you don't, talk to a school mental health professional for more help.

Case Study 4 Does not respond to auditory instruction: James

■ Case Study 4 - James

James is a third-grader whose performance seems highly variable. On some projects he does quite well and seems to be bright and capable. Other times he seems to totally miss the boat. He doesn't follow the instructions, does the wrong thing, says completely off-the-mark things in class discussions and seems to be daydreaming and off-task. His grades suffer, and often his assignments are incorrectly done. You wonder about his memory at times because he remembers spelling one day and loses it the next. You've wondered if he has attention problems, but the variability of his behavior is confusing.

 *Thinking About It*

Have you had experience with children like James? Think about those children as you work through the eight problem-solving steps.

Discussion

James is demonstrating behaviors often seen in drug-exposed children who have difficulty with auditory processing. These children have normal IQs and learning capabilities but have difficulty with memory and learning when material is presented verbally with no visual stimulation. (You sometimes see the opposite pattern as well, with children who cannot organize visual, nonverbal material but do well with verbal presentation.) Their performance tends to be highly variable, and it is often difficult to discern what the problem is without careful observation and assessment. Often these children as infants had delayed speech/language acquisition and may have received early intervention services. It is also important to know that these behaviors can be exhibited by children with trauma in their histories. Daydreaming-type behaviors can become coping strategies for children in abusive situations, and these strategies remain with the child even after he is removed from the abusive home.

Step 1: Identifying Target Behavior

Focusing Questions:

- What is the behavior I wish to change?

- Is the behavior specific and observable?

- Does the behavior occur repeatedly over time?

- Can I describe the behavior so others know exactly what I mean?

- Will the child understand what I want him to do?

- Do my colleagues agree the behavior is problematic?

- Can they confirm my perceptions on this?

Discussion:

Often the child's daydreaming, off-task behavior is the precipitant of his other achievement problems, such as not following directions or not completing assignments correctly. You would want to establish under what teaching/classroom circumstances the child daydreams, look carefully at the nature of the assignments he does correctly and incorrectly, and note what is happening when he is off-task and what brings him back to task.

Step 2: Collecting Baseline Data

Focusing Questions:

- What form of charting will help me collect information on the target behavior?

- Is frequency and duration important information to have for baseline information?

- What would be the best way to collect information on the circumstance surrounding the target behavior?

- Will collecting work samples be helpful in this case?

Discussion:

You will want to track the duration of the child's daydreaming behavior. How long does he stay off-task? What precipitates the daydreaming? How frequently do these episodes occur during the day? Most important, during what kinds of activities does the daydreaming occur? You will need to look carefully at your own behavior and the activities of the classroom to make notes that reveal this critical information.

Discussion:

You may also want to examine and link grades on assignments and tests to your observations of classroom behavior, especially when you have given instructions and the child seems to have misunderstood them.

Step 3: Evaluating Contributing Factors

Focusing Questions:

- What do I know about this child? Skill deficits? Learning/ emotional problems?

- What are the influences that cannot be changed?

- Have I asked the child to tell me about himself?

- What do I need to know about the family?

- What questions can I ask the family? What is the context of the behavior? Have I specified the exact circumstances in which the target behaviors most often occur?

- Is my style of teaching or disciplining or the classroom

- Is environment a contributing factor?

Discussion:

If you find, after looking over the frequency of daydreaming behavior, that it occurs most often during oral instruction, then you have an important clue that may indicate a dominant pattern. Check the circumstance under which the child follows directions correctly and incorrectly. You will want to discuss your observations with parents and other teachers to see if anyone else has found similar patterns. For example, a

Discussion:

mother may tell you that when the child was little she would always have the child repeat directions to be sure he was listening because most of the time he "tunes people out." Often parents also note that their child makes nonsensical comments in the middle of a conversation, or that it is very difficult to get him to follow directions because somewhere between A and B or B and C he seems to become distracted. Check with the parents about speech/language development and ask if any services were provided. The child can also report on his own experience. The child may recognize that it is hard to listen to people when they are talking, and that he finds himself thinking about something else. Finally, talking with his other teachers can help you determine if your experiences are generalizable and thus more likely to be on target.

Step 4: Identifying Appropriate Behavior to Replace the Target Behavior

Focusing Questions:

- What is the function of the behavior?

- What behavior can I substitute that will serve the same function?

Discussion:

If your baseline data and contributing factors indicate the child is able to perform visually much better than aurally, it follows that the daydreaming and off-task behavior are a function of some auditory processing problems. This results in the child completing assignments incorrectly and not fol-

Discussion:

lowing directions. You will want to think about interventions that can increase the child's on-task behavior and assist him in following directions and correctly completing of assignments. Daydreaming behaviors should, by extension, be reduced. You may need to think about how to help the child in particular subject areas where verbal learning is standard and where the child seems to have the most difficulty with retention.

Step 5: Brainstorm Possible Interventions

Focusing Questions:

- Where can I set up the intervention in my classroom?

- Do I need special resources for this intervention?

- What type of reinforcement will I use?

- Have I explained the intervention to the class? The child? The school staff and administrator?

- Do I feel comfortable trying this intervention?

- Do the baseline data indicate the need for this intervention?

- Can the intervention produce the desired change?

- Is the intervention acceptable to the child? The parents?

Discussion:

Once you have established that the child is not responding to your oral instruction and directions, you may need to do some careful self-evaluation to determine how much time

Discussion:

you devote to oral instruction and direction. You may want to tape-record your classroom activities for a day or try to record how long an interval passes without any visual information being provided. Seating these types of children close to you so you can monitor them more closely, and so fewer auditory distractions may interfere with their focus, is important. After careful thought, add a variety of multisensory activities to your classroom presentations, such as blackboard use, overheads, visual displays, etc. When you observe a child daydreaming, you may want to ask him what he is thinking about to determine if there are any personal problems that need your attention. You need to frequently prompt these children to help them get back on-task, including calling on them frequently, standing near them, or touching their shoulder. Placing their desk on a piece of carpeting can also help modulate the often loud sounds in the classroom so they are less distracted. You can also help a child begin to monitor himself by setting up a contract that will provide an incentive for correctly done assignments or less off-task behavior. It may be critical to give written as well as oral directions to the class and check on the child to be sure he has understood the assignment. You will need to work on your own teaching style to reduce the amount of class time spent in passive listening.

Step 6: Communicating Interventions to Parents and Children

Focusing Questions:

- Have the parents been included in the process?

- Has the child been included in the process?

Focusing Questions:

- Did you ask the parents and child if they have questions?

- Did you invite suggestions from the parents and child?

Discussion:

If you think a child might have an auditory processing problem, you may want to bring the school psychologist into the discussion. You will need to explain to the child that he sometimes does not pay attention and misses instruction and directions. You should ask him to give you a signal (i.e. , a red cup on his desk) when he does not understand how to do an assignment. You should describe the prompts that you will give him, your expectations of his responses, and the reward system. You may want to enlist the parents' help by providing the child a homework assignment notebook. After the child completes his assignments each afternoon, the parents can check his homework, sign the book and note any problems the child had in understanding or completing the work. Parents also need to provide the child with a quiet place to do homework. They may want to develop special visual learning aids to help their child with work that is especially hard for him.

Step 7: Implementing Selected Interventions

Focusing Questions:

- Do I have all the supplies I need?

- Do I have a start/end date?

- Do I have an evaluation plan?

Focusing Questions:

- Have I communicated with the parents and child?

- Do I have a plan to remind the child daily what is expected of him?

- Have I shown the child how to use these strategies when needed?

- Do I have a plan of consequences or reward for positive behavior?

- Have I allowed for questions and revisions with parent/child?

- Am I keeping my eye on the goal?

- Am I as flexible as I need to be?

- Am I empathic with the child?

Discussion:

These children will need frequent reminders about the intervention plan. Given their learning style, creating a visual reminder about the reward system and other cues can be very helpful. You will need to be working on your own teaching style at the same time.

Step 8: Evaluating and Revising Interventions

Focusing Questions:

- Have I allowed enough time for the intervention to work?

Focusing Questions:

- Have I created a system for comparing pre- and post-intervention?

- Have I called the parents to tell them how the intervention is progressing?

- Have I kept the same goal from beginning to end?

Discussion:

Evaluation of success in cases such as these can often be quickly accomplished by looking at the number of assignments correctly completed and turned in as compared with the number recorded in your baseline data. You will want to check with the parents on improvements or problems at home and talk to the child about whether things are any easier. You may also want to establish your own success in providing information in a variety of modalities in the classroom, including writing directions on the blackboard, underlining key words with color, and using charts and graphics. Depending on your success, you may need to increase or decrease how frequently you check with the child after an assignment is given, and you may need to have the child paraphrase what he thinks he has to do. If, however, the child shows improvement, you will want to slowly reduce the intensity of your one-to-one interventions and focus increasingly on helping the child identify for himself when he is having trouble and needs extra help.

Case Study 5 Unable to work independently/organizational difficulties: Cherie

■ Case Study 5 - Cherie

Cherie is a first-grader who came to your attention near the early part of the school year because she seemed to be having a difficult time learning the most basic skills in the first-grade curriculum. She had great difficulty completing worksheets or any other seat work, no matter what the subject matter or how it was presented. You acted quickly, and the school agreed to screen her for special education services. She qualified for LD services due to significant problems with early reading and math skills. She is now receiving "pull-out" LD services for one to two hours per day, and her basic skills are beginning to emerge on the work she is doing in her LD hour, where she is one of two students. However, you have noticed she does not demonstrate those same skills in your classroom. You talk to the LD teacher and compare notes — Cherie is not using her skills in the regular class. Instead, when given worksheets, she hides them to avoid working on them. She starts things and never finishes them, is up and out of her seat when she is supposed to be working, and is constantly looking at the work of other children. She is also constantly seeking your help and attention, but after you help her for a couple of minutes, it isn't long before she is back to her antics. Now, instead of a learning problem, you think she has a behavioral problem, and you find yourself feeling angry at this child for whom you had previously advocated because you thought she was learning disabled.

 Thinking About It

Have you had experiences with children like Cherie? Think about those children as you work through the eight problem-solving steps.

Discussion

Many of the behaviors Cherie is demonstrating are typical of children with organizational difficulties. These children are often identified as having attention problems (some do), but many are seen as being unmotivated and work avoidant and as having behavioral problems.

These are children who have a fundamental deficit in their organizational abilities and who struggle with almost all assignments they are expected to complete on their own. Oftentimes, before they get five minutes into the assignment they seem to no longer know what to do, or right after you have explained how to do something, they indicate they don't know what they are supposed to do. They seem easily distracted, very needy and to want exclusive attention when working on something. Often, as in the case above, these children will demonstrate highly variable skills and abilities. They will be able to complete certain kinds of work in one environment and will be unable to perform the same work in another environment. Thus, one of the defining features of these children is the variability of their performance and behavior. Some do well in verbal tasks but can't perform on nonverbal tasks, and for others verbally oriented tasks seem impossible while nonverbal tasks are easier. In many of these cases, the underlying problem is one of organization; they do not know how to structure and organize the work they are asked to complete without tremendous external support. Thus they will do well one on one but not in a larger classroom situation. Parents often complain that homework takes forever and that they have to work with the children for them to be at all successful. In addition, these children often don't do well during unstructured activities (i.e., when they are given an opportunity to draw what they want) or during free time when they are expected to provide their own structure and activity. These behaviors also can be accompanied by characteristics of attention-deficit disorder (hyperactivity). Drug-exposed children often have great difficulty with self-organization and lack the ability to impose structure themselves.

Step 1: Identifying Target Behavior

Focusing Questions:

- What is the behavior I wish to change?

- Is the behavior specific and observable?

- Does the behavior occur repeatedly over time?

- Can I describe the behavior so others know exactly what I mean?

Focusing Questions:

- Will the child understand what I want him to do?

- Do my colleagues agree the behavior is problematic?

- Can they confirm my perceptions on this?

Discussion:

It is unlikely the teacher of a child with organizational deficits will recognize this pattern at this point in the problem-solving process. Rather, the target behaviors that are likely to be problematic and thus identified as targets will include not finishing her seat work and/or homework; getting into trouble during unstructured time; cheating from other students; constantly seeking the help and attention of the teacher; being off-task during independent seat work; not working to her ability (as seen on other kinds of work assignments). Thus, all these behaviors are likely candidates for target behavior, and it will be the details that allow the teacher to see the pattern that indicates organizational problems.

Step 2: Collecting Baseline Data

Focusing Questions:

- What form of charting will help me collect information on the target behavior?

- Is frequency and duration important information to have for baseline information?

- What would be the best way to collect information on the circumstance surrounding the target behavior?

- Will collecting work samples be helpful in this case?

Discussion:

In order to pick up on the underlying problem of organization, it will be critical to collect data not only on the frequency and duration of the target behavior, but also on the range of context variables we have already discussed. These include the specific nature of the work being done, the classroom environment, the amount of structure provided by the given activity. You probably also will need to record information about when the child is most successful in completing her work so you can compare it to when she is unsuccessful in order to discover patterns.

Step 3: Evaluating Contributing Factors

Focusing Questions:

- What do I know about this child? Skill deficits? Learning/emotional problems?

- What are the influences that cannot be changed?

- Have I asked the child to tell me about himself?

- What do I need to know about the family?

- What questions can I ask the family?

- What is the context of the behavior? Have I specified the exact circumstances in which the target behaviors most often occur?

- Is my style of teaching or disciplining or the classroom environment a contributing factor?

Discussion:

As you look at your baseline data ask yourself about the patterns that emerge. The question of organizational capabilities should be among those you ask yourself as you view your data. Does the child have problems when asked to work independently? Does the child cheat or constantly seek help happen when you give her a less structured assignment? How does the child respond to unstructured nonwork time? Is she able to pick an activity and engage in it appropriately on her own? Is she most successful in highly structured classroom work? As you sit down and talk to the parents about the behaviors you have noticed, you are likely to hear about homework problems. You also may hear about the child's difficulty playing on her own, her difficulty getting through complex tasks (because she seems to get lost in the middle), and the parents' feeling of exhaustion as you discuss how much attention their child needs.

Step 4: Identifying Appropriate Behavior to Replace the Target Behavior

Focusing Questions:

- What is the function of the behavior?

- What behavior can I substitute that will serve the same function?

Discussion:

These children lack a fundamental capacity to work independently without an external source providing a clearly delineated structure and organization. Your goal would be

Discussion:

to help build this capacity in the child by providing the basic tools of problem-solving, thinking things through step by step, and developing sequences of behavioral action. Specific interventions may include asking for help; developing problem-solving steps that allow her to begin to work independently; setting up check lists that help impose organization and keep the child on track; and monitoring the level of organization in your teaching style and materials.

Step 5: Brainstorm Possible Interventions

Focusing Questions:

- Where can I set up the intervention in my classroom?

- Do I need special resources for this intervention?

- What type of reinforcement will I use?

- Have I explained the intervention to the class? The child? The school staff and administrator?

- Do I feel comfortable trying this intervention?

- Do the baseline data indicate the need for this intervention?

- Can the intervention produce the desired change?

- Is the intervention acceptable to the child? The parents?

Discussion:

In working with children with this kind of skill deficit, the interventions we introduce are intended to increase the

Discussion:

child's fundamental capacity to exhibit certain adaptive behaviors and skills. It is thus critical that the efforts made are positive and reinforcing in nature, not punitive or angry. Helping a child understand and monitor her progress can be enhanced by using charts, stickers and rewards that emphasize her new competencies and efforts. You may want to pair the child with someone in the class who is good at organizing and can coach her. This may help her avoid cheating behaviors and stop seeking so much attention from the teacher. As in some of the other cases discussed, there needs to be a fundamental shift in how the teacher views and understands the child's needs, what the function of the disruptive behavior is, and how the classroom environment and work expectations hinder or help the child who cannot independently organize her work. Thus some brainstorming efforts need to be aimed at adapting your style and expectations to meet the needs of this child. Perhaps the child can check in with you at regular intervals during an assignment, as designated on her work with stars or stickers. This can both provide organization and help her feel less overwhelmed when looking at an assignment. Limiting distractions can be beneficial, as and having the child cover up everything but what she is working on can reduce organizational overload. Providing praise when a child asks for help appropriately, rather than cheating or disturbing others, may also be effective. Again, prevention is key. Sitting and helping the child organize her efforts and behavior before the problem arises will save you much time in the long run. This should include walking through the assignment, as well as developing a plan for what to do during free time, recess, or any other unstructured time during which she does not organize well.

Step 6: Communicating Interventions to Parents and Children

Focusing Questions:

- Has the parent been included in the process?

- Has the child been included in the process?

- Did you ask the parents and child if they have questions?

- Did you invite suggestions from the parent(s) and child?

Discussion:

While the parents likely have had many experiences with their child that correspond to your own, they may not yet have a way of thinking about their child's needs and what they might be able to do to increase her capabilities. You will want them to start observing behavior at home and interpreting it in ways comparable to your own, so homework time can be structured in similar ways, with appropriate help, expectations and goals being provided. They may be able to adapt many of the ideas you are using in the classroom to the child's world at home. This includes the child's organizing herself to complete chores, self-help skills and structured play activities, as well as homework. The child has to be told what the parents expect her to be able to do, how they are available to her for help, and what avoidant or disruptive behaviors are to be disallowed, with the accompanying explanation of what she <u>should</u> do.

Step 7: Implementing Selected Interventions

Focusing Questions:

- Do I have all the supplies I need?

- Do I have a start/end date?

Focusing Questions:

- Do I have an evaluation plan?

- Have I communicated with the parents and child?

- Do I have a plan to remind the child daily what is expected of him?

- Have I shown the child how to use these strategies when needed?

- Do I have a plan of consequences or reward for positive behavior?

- Have I allowed for questions and revisions with parent/child?

- Am I keeping my eye on the goal?

- Am I as flexible as I need to be?

- Am I empathic with the child?

Discussion:

Regular reminders about the plan, the expected behaviors and any rewards or incentives you are using will be critical, as the child will not likely be able to remember and use the plan well without extra assistance. You may want to explain the situation to the entire class so they can assist and be understanding. Remember, time spent upfront helping the child and preventing problems is time gained on the other end when you would normally be punishing, discussing, or frustrated and angry.

Step 6: Communicating Interventions to Parents and Children

Focusing Questions:

- Have I allowed enough time for the intervention to work?

- Have I created a system for comparing pre- and post-intervention?

- Have I called the parents to tell them how the intervention   is progressing?

- Have I kept the same goal from beginning to end?

Discussion:

You will want to keep track of some of the same behaviors you collected at the beginning of this process to determine if these interventions have reduced their frequency. It may also be helpful to track completion of work, grades, and overall learning. In working with this child, you are trying to develop a capacity that does not exist. This is a process that takes time, but it's one in which you should also be able to see subtle improvement. Over time you will want to reduce the intensity of the intervention, modify your expectations and change your goals. However, this needs to be done slowly and only with evidence that the child is ready. This child likely will continue to show variable capabilities, depending on the larger environment, the task at hand and the degree of structure of the activity. Helping others in the school understand the framework and function of the child's behavior will be very helpful for everyone.

In this section, *Toward One on One: Group and Individual Behavior Interventions,* we have examined principles of behavior management, ways of recording baseline data and characteristics of effective Individual Interventions. We also have introduced the problem-solving process and applied it to real NAFARE case studies. Finally, we have presented five one-on-one intervention templates and have demonstrated how different strategies relate to specific behavioral problems.

By this point, you have been exposed to a wide range of information and ideas that relate to your interaction with children affected by prenatal drug exposure:

1. There are both biologic and environmental factors that affect children's behavior, prenatal exposure to drugs being only one of many problems that children face.

2. The behaviors seen in children affected by prenatal or environmental exposure to drugs are similar to the behaviors of many high-risk children. You can, however, use the specific strategies provided both to prevent and intervene in children's disruptive behaviors.

With this information, you can make a difference for children in your classroom, improving their academic achievement and social development by addressing their behavioral difficulties.

References

Section One

Abidin, R.R. *Parenting Stress Index, Third Edition*. Odessa, FL: Psychological Assessment Resources, Inc., 1995.

Achenbach, T.M. *Manual for the Child Behavior Checklist and 1991 Profile*. Burlington, VT: University of Vermont, Department of Psychiatry, 1991a.

Achenbach, T.M. *Manual for the Teacher's Report Form and 1991 Profile*. Burlington, VT: University of Vermont, Department of Psychiatry, 1991b.

Anastasi, A. *Psychological Testing*, 6th Edition. New York: Macmillan, 1990.

Azuma, S.D., and Chasnoff, I.J. Outcome of children prenatally exposed to cocaine and other drugs: A path analysis of three-year data. *Pediatrics* 1993;92:396-402.

Bayley, N. *Bayley Scales of Infant Development-Second Edition*. New York: Psychological Corporation, 1993.

Block, J., Block, J H., and Keyes, S. Longitudinally foretelling drug usage in adolescence: Early childhood personality and environmental precursors. *Child Development* 1988;59:336-355.

Chasnoff, I.J., Burns, W.J., Schnoll, S.H., and Burns, K.A. Phencyclidine: Effects on the fetus and neonate. *Developmental Pharmacology and Therapeutics* 1983; 6: 404 - 408.

Chasnoff, I.J., Burns, W.J., Schnoll, S.H., and Burns, K.A. Cocaine use in pregnancy. *New England Journal of Medicine* 1985;313:666-669.

Chasnoff, I.J., Griffith, D.R., MacGregor, S., Dirkes, K., and Burns, K.A. Temporal patterns of cocaine use in pregnancy. *Journal of the American Medical Association* 1989a;161:1741-1744.

Chavez, G.F., Mulinare, J., and Cordero, J. Maternal cocaine use during early pregnancy as a risk factor for congenital urogenital anomalies. *Journal of the American Medical Association* 1989;262:795-798.

Connors, C.K. (1990) *Manual for Connors' Rating Scales.* Multi-Health Systems, Inc., North Tonawanda, N.Y.

Coons C., Gay E., Fandal A., Ker C., and Frankenburg W. *The Home Screening Questionnaire Reference Manual.* Denver: Denver Developmental Materials Inc., 1981.

Davies, W. H., Zucker, R. A., Noll, R.N., and Fitzgerald, H.E. *Parental psychopathology and child-rearing practices in young alcoholic families.* Paper presented at the Meetings of the Research Society on Alcoholism. Beaver Creek, CO, June 1989.

Davis, E. Cocaine babies grow up. *NEA Today*, 1993;11:13.

Eisen, L.N., Field, T.M., Bandstra, E.S., Roberts, J.P., Morrow, C., Larson, S.K., and Steele, B.M. Perinatal cocaine effects on neonatal stress behavior and performance on the Brazelton Scale. *Pediatrics* 1991;88:477-480.

Finnegan, L.P., Connaughton, J.F., Kron, R.E., Samuels, S.J., and Batra, K.K. Neonatal abstinence syndrome: Assessment and management. In *Perinatal Addiction*, Harbison, R. D. (ed.). New York: Spectrum Publications, 1975. pp 141-158.

Frank, D.A., Bauchner, H., Parker, S., Huber, A.M., Kyei-Aboagye, K., Cabral, H., and Zuckerman, B. Neonatal body proportionality and body composition after in-utero exposure to cocaine and marijuana. *Journal of Pediatrics* 1990;117:622-626.

Fried, P.A., and Watkinson, B. 36-and 48-month neurobehavioral follow-up of children prenatally exposed to marijuana, cigarettes, and alcohol. *Developmental and Behavioral Pediatrics* 1990;11(2):49-58.

Gordon, M. *The Gordon Diagnostic System (GDS)*. Dewitt, NY: Gordon Systems, 1986.

Griffith, D.R. The effects of perinatal cocaine exposure on infant neurobehavior and early maternal-infant interactions. In: Chasnoff, I.J. (ed) *Drugs, Alcohol, Pregnancy and Parenting.* Lancaster, UK: Kluwer Academic Publishers, 1988.

Hamilton, E.B. *The relationship of maternal patterns of stress, coping, and support to quality of early infant-mother attachment.* Unpublished doctoral dissertation, University of Virginia, Charlottesville.

Hurt, H., Brodsky, N.L., Betancourt, L., Braitman, L.E., Malmud, E., Giannetta, J. Cocaine-exposed children: follow-up through 30 months. *Journal of Substance Abuse* 1995;7(3):267-80.

Hutchings, D.E., and Dow-Edwards, D. Animal models of opiate, cocaine and cannabis use. In *Chemical Dependency and Pregnancy: Clinics in Perinatalogy.* Chasnoff, I. J. (ed.). Philadelphia: W.B. Saunders Co.,1988. pp 1-22.

Jones, K.L., Smith, D.W., Ulleland, C.N., and Streissguth, A.P. Pattern of malformation in offspring of chronic alcoholic mothers. *Lancet* 1973;1:1267-1271.

Kandel, D., Simcha-Fagan, O., and Davis, M. Risk factors from delinquency and illicit drug use from adolescence to young adulthood. *Journal of Drug Issues,*1986; 60:67-90.

Kaufman A., and Kaufman N. *Kaufman Test of Education Achievement.* Circle Pines, MN: American Guidance Service, 1985.

Kellam, S.G., Brown, C.H., Rubin, B.R., and Emsminger, M.E. Paths leading to teenage psychiatric symptoms and substance use: Development epidemiological studies in Woodlawn. In: S.B. Guze, F.J. Earls, and J.E. Barret (eds.) *Childhood Psychopathology and Development.* New York, 1983.

Kronstadt, D. *Pregnancy and Cocaine Addiction: An Overview of Impact and Treatment.* Far West Laboratory for Educational Research and Development. San Francisco, 1989.

Lester, B.M., Corwin, M.J., Sepkoski, C., Seifer, R., Peucher, M., McLaughlin, S. and Golum, H.L. Neurobehavioral syndromes in cocaine-exposed newborn infants. *Child Development* 1991;62:694-705.

Mayes, L.C., Bornstein, M.H., Chawarska, K., and Granger, R.H. Information processing and developmental assessments in three-month-old infants exposed prenatally to cocaine. *Pediatrics* 1995;95:539-545.

McConaughy, S.H. Evaluating behavioral and emotional disorders with CBCL, TRF, and YSR cross-informant scales. *Journal of Emotional and Behavioral Disorders* 1993;1:40-52.

National Institute on Drug Abuse. *National Pregnancy and Health Survey.* Rockville, MD: U.S. Department of Health and Human Services, 1994.

Nulman, I., Rovet, J., Altmann, D., Bradley, C., Einarson, T., and Koren, G. Neurodevelopment of adopted children exposed in utero to cocaine [see comments]. *Journal of Development and Behavioral Pediatrics* 1995 Dec;16(6):418-24; discussion 425-30.

Nye, C.L., Zucker, R.A., Fitzgerald, H.E., Early intervention in the path to alcohol problems through conduct problems: treatment involvement and child behavior change *Journal of Consulting Clinical Psychology* 1995 Oct;63(5):831-40.

Orlandi, M.A., Weston, R. and Epstein, L.G. Cultural Competence for Evaluators. Rockville, MD: U.S. Department of Health and Human Services, DHHS Publication no. (ADM)92-1884, Office for Substance Abuse Prevention, 1992.

Ornoy, A., Michailevskaya, V., Lukashov, I., Bar-Hamburger, R., and Harel, S. The developmental outcome of children born to heroin-dependent mothers, raised at home or adopted. *Canadian Medical Association Journal of Medicine* 1994 Dec 1;151(11):1591-7.

Oulellette, E.M., Rosett, H.L., Rosman, N.P., et al. Adverse effects on offspring of maternal alcohol abuse during pregnancy. *New England Journal of Medicine* 1977;297:528-531.

Rutter, M. Resilience in the face of adversity: protective factors and resistance to psychiatric disorder. *British Journal of Psychiatry* 1985;147:598-611.

Sameroff, A.J., Barocas, R., and Seifer, R. The early development of children born to mentally ill women. In: Watt, N.F., Antony, E.J., Wynne, L.C., Rolf, J., eds. *Children at Risk for Schizophrenia: a Longitudinal Perspective.* Cambridge, England: Cambridge University Press, 1984.

Seifer, R. and Sameroff, A.J. Multiple determinants of risk and invulnerability. In: Antony, E.J., Cohler, B.J., eds. *The Invulnerable Child.* New York: The Guilford Press, 1987:51-69.

Sher, K.J., Walitzer, K.S., Wood, P., and Brent, E.E. Characteristics of children of alcoholics: Putative risk factors, substance use and abuse, and psychopathology. *Journal of Abnormal Psychology* 1991; 100: 427-448.

Singer, L.T., Garber, R., and Kliegman, R. Neurobehavioral sequelae of fetal cocaine exposure. *Journal of Pediatrics* 1991;119:667-672.

Stanger C., McConaughy, S., and Achenbach, T. Three-year course of behavioral/emotional problems in a national sample of 4- to 16-year olds: II. Predictors of syndromes. *Journal of the American Academy of Child and adolescent Psychiatry* 1992;31:941-950.

Stoneman, Z., Brody, G.H., and Burke, M. Marital quality, depression, and inconsistent parenting: Relationship with observed mother-child conflict. *American Journal of Orthopsychiatry* 1989; 59:105-117.

Streissguth, A., Sampson, P., and Barr, H. Neurobehavioral dose-response effects of prenatal alcohol exposure in humans from infancy to adulthood. *Annals of the New York Academy of Sciences* 1989;562:145-158.

Sunseri, A.J., Alberti, J.M., Kent, N.D., Schoenberger, J.A., Sunseri, J.K., Amuwo, S., and Vickers, P. Reading, demographic, social and psychological factors related to pre-adolescent smoking and nonsmoking behaviors and attitudes. *Journal of School Health* 1983 Apr;53(4):257-63.

Thorndike, R.L., Hagen, E.P., and Sattler, J.M. *Stanford-Binet Intelligence Scale: 4th Edition.* Chicago: Riverside Publishing Co., 1986.

Ullman, R.K., Sleator, E.K., and Sprague, R.L., ADD-H: *Comprehensive Teacher's Rating Scale (ACTERS) 2nd ed.*

Wechsler, D. *WPPSI-R Manual.* Chicago: The Psychological Corporation, 1989.

Wechsler, D. *WISC-III Manual.* Chicago:The Psychological Corporation, 1991.

Werner, E.E. High-risk children in young adulthood: a longitudinal study from birth to 32 years. *Am Journal of Orthopsychiatry* 1989;61:6-22.

West, M.O. and Prinz, R.J. Parental alcoholism and childhood psycho-pathology. In: S. Chess, A. Thomas, and M.E. Hertzig (eds.) *Annual Progress in Child Psychiatry and Child Development.* New York: Brunner/Mazel, 1988.

Wilkes, D. Children exposed to drugs: Meeting their needs. In: J. Follman (ed.) *Hot Topics: Usable Research.* Greensboro, NC: Southeastern Regional Vision for Education.

Yoshikawa, H. Prevention as cumulative protection: effects of early family support and education on chronic delinquency and its risks. *Psychological Bulletin* 1994;115:28-54.

Zareski, J.R. Prematurity and the single parent: effects of cumulative stress on child development. Unpublished doctoral dissertation, University of Virginia, Charlottesville.

Section Two

Ashton-Warner, Syvia (1963) *Teacher* . New York: Simon and Schuster

Brofenbrenner, U., (1979) *The Ecology of Human Development.* Cambridge: Harvard University Press

Braswell, L., and Bloomquist, M. (1991) *Cognitive-behavioral therapy with ADHD children: Child, family, and school interventions.* New York: Guilford Press.

Brophy, J. (1966) *Motivating Students to Learn.* New York: McGraw Hill

Charney, R.S., (1992) *Teaching Children to Care: Responsive Management in the Classroom.* MA: Northeast Foundation for Children

Driekurs, R., Grunwald, B.B., Pepper, F.C., (1982) *Maintaining Sanity in the Classroom: Classroom Management Techniques.* NY: Harper and Row.

Delapenha, L.(1991) *Strategies for Teaching Young Children Prenatally Exposed to Drugs.* Perinatal Addiction Research and Education Update, March.

Dorris, M. (1989) *The Broken Cord.* New York: HarperCollins Publishers

Johnson, D.W. *Circles of Learning: Cooperation in the Classroom,* MN: Interaction Book Co.

Kazdin, A., (1989) *Behavior Modification in Applied Settings,* CA: Brooks/ Cole.

Piaget, J., (1965) *The Moral Judgement of the Child,* NY: Macmillan.

Section Three

Ginot, Haim (1956) *Between Teacher and Child.* NY: Avon Books.

Suggested Readings

ADOPTION/FOSTER CARE

Barth, R. P., & Needell, B. (1996). Outcomes for drug-exposed children four years post-adoption. *Children and Youth Services Review, 18*(1-2), 37-56.

Chasnoff, I.J. (1993) *Guidelines for Adopting Drug Exposed Children,* Chicago, IL: National Association for Families and Addiction Research and Education.

Franck, E. J. (1996). Prenatally drug-exposed children in out-of-home care: Are we looking at the whole picture? *Child Welfare, 75*(1), 19-34.

Halfon, N., Berkowitz, G., & Klee, L. (1993). Development of an integrated case management program for vulnerable children. *Child Welfare, 72*(4), 379-396.

ALCOHOL

Abel, E. L. (1995). An update on incidence of FAS: FAS is not an equal opportunity birth defect. *Neurotoxicology & Teratology, 17*(4), 437-443.

Abel, E. L., & Hannigan, J. H. (1995). Maternal risk factors in fetal alcohol syndrome: Provocative and permissive influences. *Neurotoxicology & Teratology, 17*(4), 445-462.

Burd, L., & Moffatt, M. E. (1994). Epidemiology of fetal alcohol syndrome in American Indians, Alaskan Natives, and Canadian Aboriginal peoples: A review of the literature. *Public Health Reports, 109*(5), 688-693.

Duerbeck, N. B. (1997). Fetal alcohol syndrome. *Comprehensive Therapy,* *23*(3), 179-183.

Hankin, J. R., & Sokol, R. J. (1995). Identification and care of problems associated with alcohol ingestion in pregnancy. *Seminars in Perinatology, 19*(4), 286-292.

Holzman, C., Paneth, N., Little, R., & Pinto-Martin, J. (1995). Perinatal brain injury in premature infants born to mothers using alcohol in pregnancy: Neonatal Brain Hemorrhage Study Team. *Pediatrics, 95*(1), 66-73.

Lewis, D. D., & Woods, S. E. (1994). Fetal alcohol syndrome. *American Family Physician, 50*(5), 1025-1032.

Riley, E. P., Mattson, S. N., Sowell, E. R., Jernigan, T. L., Sobel, D. F., & Jones, K. L. (1995). Abnormalities of the corpus callosum in children prenatally exposed to alcohol. *Alcoholism, Clinical & Experimental Research, 19*(5), 1198-1202.

Wekselman, K., Spiering, K., Hetteberg, C., Kenner, C., & Flandermeyer, A. (1995). Fetal alcohol syndrome from infancy through childhood: A review of the literature. *Journal of Pediatric Nursing, 10*(5), 296-303.

COCAINE, CRACK, AND STIMULANTS

Azuma, S.D. and Chasnoff, I.J. (1993). Outcome of children prenatally exposed to cocaine and other drugs: A path analysis of three-year data. *Pediatrics, 92*, 396-402.

Barton, S. J., Harrigan, R., & Tse, A. M. (1995). Prenatal cocaine exposure: Implications for practice, policy development, and needs for future research. *Journal of Perinatology, 5*(1), 10-22.

Catanzarite, V. A. (1995). "Crystal" and pregnancy — methamphetamine-associated maternal deaths. *Western Journal of Medicine, 162*(5), 454-457.

Chasnoff, I. J. (1992). Cocaine, pregnancy, and the growing child. *Current Problems in Pediatrics, 22*(7), 302-21.

Chasnoff, I. J, Griffith DR, Freier C, and Murry J. (1992) Cocaine/polydrug use in pregnancy: Two year followup. *Pediatrics, 89*, 284-289.

Dungy-Poythress, L. J. (1995). Cocaine effects on pregnancy and infant outcome: Do we really know how bad it is? *Journal of the Association for Academic Minority Physicians, 6*(1), 46-50.

Kane, D. J., Aronson, R. A., & Zotti, M. E. (1997). The long-term effects of cocaine use during pregnancy—reasons for hope. *Wisconsin Medical Journal, 96*(2), 37-40.

King, T. A., Perlman, J. M., Laptook, A. R., Rollins, N., Jackson, G., & Little, B. (1995). Neurologic manifestations of in utero cocaine exposure in near-term and term infants. *Pediatrics, 96*(2 Pt 1), 259-264.

McCalla, S., Feldman, J., Webbeh, H., Ahmadi, R., & Minkoff, H. L. (1995). Changes in perinatal cocaine use in an inner-city hospital, 1988 to 1992. *American Journal of Public Health, 85*(12), 1695-1697.

Snodgrass, S. R. (1994). Cocaine babies: A result of multiple teratogenic influences. *Journal of Child Neurology, 9*(3), 227-233.

Tronick, E. Z., Frank, D. A., Cabral, H., Mirochnick, M., & Zuckerman, B. (1996). Late dose-response effects of prenatal cocaine exposure on newborn neurobehavioral performance. *Pediatrics, 98*(1), 76-83.

Zuckerman, B., & Frank, D. A. (1992). "Crack kids": not broken. *Pediatrics, 89*(2), 337-339.

DEVELOPMENT

Azuma, S. D., & Chasnoff, I. J. (1993). Outcome of children prenatally exposed to cocaine and other drugs: A path analysis of three-year data. *Pediatrics, 92*, 396-402.

Brooks-Gunn, J., McCarton, C., & Hawley, T. (1994). Effects of in utero drug exposure on children's development: Review & Recommendations. *Archives of Pediatrics & Adolescent Medicine, 148*(1), 33-39.

Chasnoff, I.J. (1997). Prenatal exposure to cocaine and other drugs: Is there a profile? In: Accardo, P.J., Shapiro, B.K., and Capute, A.J. (eds.) *Behavior Belongs in the Brain.* Baltimore, MD: York Press.

Elsner, J. (1995). Neurobehavioral abnormalities induced by prenatal exposure to substances of abuse — stating the problems. *Archives of Toxicology (Supplement), 17*, 221-232.

Gerber, S. E., Epstein, L., & Mencher, L. S. (1995). Recent changes in the etiology of hearing disorders: Perinatal drug exposure. *Journal of the American Academy of Audiology, 6*(5), 371-377.

Griffith, D. R., Azuma, S. D., & Chasnoff, I. J. (1994). Three-year outcome of children exposed prenatally to drugs. *Journal of the American Academy of Child & Adolescent Psychiatry, 33*(1), 20-27.

Hawley, T. L. (1994). The development of cocaine-exposed children. *Current Problems in Pediatrics, 24*(8), 259-266.

Hofkosh, D., Pringle, J. L., Wald, H. P., Switala, J., Hinderliter, S. A., & Hamel, S. C. (1995). Early interactions between drug-involved mothers and infants: Within group differences. *Archives of Pediatrics & Adolescent Medicine, 149*(6), 665-672.

Howard, J., Beckwith, L., Espinosa, M., & Tyler, R. (1995). Development of infants born to cocaine-abusing women: Biologic/maternal influences. *Neurotoxicology & Teratology, 17*(4), 403-411.

Hurt, H., Brodsky, N. L., Betancourt, L., Braitman, L. E., Malmud, E., & Giannetta, J. (1995). Cocaine-exposed children: Follow-up through 30 months. *Journal of Developmental & Behavioral Pediatrics, 16*(1), 29-35.

Larroque, B., Kaminski, M., Dehaene, P., Subtil, D., Delfosse, M. J., & Querleu, D. (1995). Moderate prenatal alcohol exposure and psychomotor development at preschool age. *American Journal of Public Health, 85*(12), 1654-1661.

Lester, B. M., Tronick, E. Z. (1994). The effects of prenatal cocaine exposure and child outcome. Special Issue: Prenatal drug exposure and child outcome. *Infant Mental Health Journal, 15*(2), 107-120.

Mayes, L. C., Bornstein, M. H., Chawarska, K., & Granger, R. H. (1995). Information processing and developmental assessments in 3-month-old infants exposed prenatally to cocaine. *Pediatrics, 95*(4), 539-545.

National Institute on Drug Abuse (NIDA). (1996). *NIDA Research Monograph Series: No. 164. Behavioral studies of drug-exposed offspring: Methodological issues in human and animal research* (NIH Publication No. 96-4105). Washington, DC: U. S. Government Printing Office.

Richardson, G. A., Day, N. L., & Goldschmidt, L. (1995). Prenatal alcohol, marijuana, and tobacco use: Infant mental and motor development. *Neurotoxicology & Teratology, 17*(4), 479-487.

Scherling, D. (1994). Prenatal cocaine exposure and childhood psychopathology: A developmental analysis. *American Journal of Orthopsychiatry, 64*(1), 9-19.

Soepatmi, S. (1994). Developmental outcomes of children of mothers dependent on heroin or heroin/methadone during pregnancy. *Acta Paediatrica, 404*(Supplement), 36-39.

HALLUCINOGENS

Glantz, J. C., Woods, J. R., Jr. (1993). Cocaine, heroin, and phencyclidine: Obstetric perspectives. *Clinical Obstetrics & Gynecology, 36*(2), 279-301.

Rahbar, F., Fomufod, A., White, D., & Westney, L. S. (1993). Impact of intrauterine exposure to phencyclidine (PCP) and cocaine on neonates. *Journal of the National Medical Association, 85*(5), 349-352.

LEGAL AND POLICY ISSUES

American Academy of Pediatrics Committee on Substance Abuse. (1995). Drug-exposed infants. *Pediatrics, 96*(2 Pt 1), 364-367.

Andrews, A. B., & Patterson, E. G. (1995). Searching for solutions to alcohol and other drug abuse during pregnancy: Ethics, values, and constitutional principles. *Social Work, 40*(1), 55-64.

Burns, D. L. (1997). Positive toxicology screening in newborns: Ethical issues in the decision to legally intervene. *Pediatric nursing, 23*(1), 73-75.

Madden, R. G. (1993). State actions to control fetal abuse: Ramifications for child welfare practice. *Child Welfare, 72*(2), 129-140.

Millard, D. D. (1996). Toxicology testing in neonates: Is it ethical, and what does it mean? *Clinics in Perinatology, 23*(3), 491-507.

Poland, M. L., Dombrowski, M. P., Ager, J. W., & Sokol, R. J. (1993). Punishing pregnant drug users: Enhancing the flight from care. *Drug & Alcohol Dependence, 31*(3), 199-203.

Sagatun-Edwards, I. J., Saylor, C., & Shifflett, B. (1995). Drug exposed infants in the social welfare system and juvenile court. *Child Abuse & Neglect, 19*(1), 83-91.

Schroedel, J. R., & Peretz, P. (1994). A gender analysis of policy formation: The case of fetal abuse. *Journal of Health Politics, Policy & Law, 19*(2), 335-360.

MARIJUANA

Dreher, M. C., Nugent, K., & Hudgins, R. (1994). Prenatal marijuana exposure and neonatal outcomes in Jamaica: An ethnographic study. *Pediatrics, 93*(2), 254-260.

Fried, P. A. (1995). Prenatal exposure to marihuana and tobacco during infancy, early and middle childhood: Effects and an attempt at synthesis. *Archives of Toxicology, 17*, 233-260.

Musty, R. E., Reggio, P., & Consroe, P. (1995). A review of recent advances in cannabinoid research and the 1994 International Symposium on Cannabis and the Cannabinoids. *Life Sciences, 56*(23-24), 1933-1940.

Shiono, P. H., Klebanoff, M. A., Nugent, R. P., Cotch, M. F., Wilkins, D. G., Rollins, D. E., Carey, J. C., & Behrman, R. E. (1995). The impact of cocaine and marijuana use on low birth weight and preterm birth: A multicenter study. *American Journal of Obstetrics & Gynecology, 172*(1 Pt 1), 19-27.

NARCOTICS

DePetrillo, P. B., & Rice, J. M. (1995). Methadone dosing and pregnancy: Impact on program compliance. *International Journal of the Addictions, 30*(2), 207-217.

Hagopian, G. S., Wolfe, H. M., Sokol, R. J., Ager, J. W., Wardell, J. N., & Cepeda, E. E. (1996). Neonatal outcome following methadone exposure in utero. *Journal of Maternal & Fetal Medicine, 5*(6), 348-354.

Hickey, J. E., Suess, P. E., Newlin, D. B., Spurgeon, L., & Porges, S. W. (1995). Vagal tone regulation during sustained attention in boys exposed to opiates in utero. *Addictive Behaviors, 20*(1), 43-59.

Jarvis, M. A., & Schnoll, S. H. (1994). Methadone treatment during pregnancy. *Journal of Psychoactive Drugs, 26*(2), 155-161.

Kaltenbach, K. A. (1994). Effects of in-utero opiate exposure: New paradigms for old questions. *Drug & Alcohol Dependence, 36*(2), 83-87.

Thomas, D. B. (1995). Cleft palate, mortality and morbidity in infants of substance abusing mothers. *Journal of Pediatrics & Child Health, 31*(5), 457-460.

PATERNAL SUBSTANCE ABUSE

Cicero, T. J., Nock, B., O'Connor, L., Adams, M., & Meyer, E. R. (1995). Adverse effects of paternal opiate exposure on offspring development and sensitivity to morphine-induced analgesia. *Journal of Pharmacology & Experimental Therapeutics, 273*(1), 386-392.

Cleary, S., & Freeman, K. (1994). Exploring the link between Fetal Alcohol Syndrome and sociopathic behavior. *Free Inquiry in Creative Sociology, 22*(2), 138-143.

Little, J., & Vainio, H. (1994). Mutagenic lifestyles? A review of evidence of associations between germ-cell mutations in humans and smoking, alcohol consumption and use of "recreational" drugs. *Mutation Research, 313*(2-3), 131-151.

Olshan, A. F., & Savitz, D. A. (1995). Paternal smoking and low birthweight: The routes of exposure. *American Journal of Public Health, 85*(8 Pt 1), 1169-1170.

Savitz, D. A., Zhang, J., Schwingl, P., & John, E. M. (1992). Association of paternal alcohol use with gestational age and birth weight. *Teratology, 46*(5), 465-471.

Windham, G. C., Fenster, L., Hopkins, B., & Swan, S. H. (1995). The association of moderate maternal and paternal alcohol consumption with birthweight and gestational age. *Epidemiology, 6*(6), 591-597.

PRESCRIPTION DRUGS

Fitzgerald, M. (1995). Prescription and over-the-counter drug use during pregnancy. *Journal of the American Academy of Nurse Practitioners, 7*(2), 87-89.

Nulman, I., Rovet, J., Stewart, D. E., Wolpin, J., Gardner, H. A., Theis, J. G., Kulin, N., & Koren, G. (1997). Neurodevelopment of children exposed in utero to antidepressant drugs. *New England Journal of Medicine, 336*(4), 258-262.

Rayburn, W. F. (1993). A physician's prerogative to prescribe drugs for off-label uses during pregnancy. *Obstetrics & Gynecology, 81*(6), 1052-1055.

Rubin, J. D., Ferencz, C., & Loffredo, C. (1993). Use of prescription and non-prescription drugs in pregnancy: The Baltimore-Washington Infant Study Group. *Journal of Clinical Epidemiology, 46*(6), 582-589.

PREVALENCE

Dempsey, M. E., Schlechte, T., Stockbauer, J. W., Schramm, W. F., Cary, P. L. (1996). Prevalence and implications of perinatal substance use in Missouri. *Missouri Medicine, 93*(6), 292-299.

Dicker, M., & Leighton, E. A. (1994). Trends in the US prevalence of drug-using parturient women and drug-affected newborns, 1979 through 1990. *American Journal of Public Health, 84*(9), 1433-1438.

Jacob, J., Harrison, H., Jr., Tigert, A. T. (1995). Prevalence of alcohol and illicit drug use by expectant mothers. *Alaska Medicine, 37*(3), 83-87.

Kokotailo, P. K., Langhough, R. E., Cox, N. S., Davidson, S. R., & Fleming, M. F. (1994). Cigarette, alcohol and other drug use among small city pregnant adolescents. *Journal of Adolescent Health, 15*(5), 366-373.

Lake, M. F., Angel, J. L., Murphy, J. M., & Poekert, G. (1992). Patterns of illicit drug use at the time of labor in a private and public hospital. *Journal of Perinatology, 12*(2), 134-136.

McCalla, S., Feldman, J., Webbeh, H., Ahmadi, R., Minkoff, H. L. (1995). Changes in perinatal cocaine use in an inner-city hospital, 1988 to 1992. *American Journal of Public Health, 85*(12), 1695-1697.

National Institute on Drug Abuse. (1996). *National Pregnancy & Health Survey: Drug Use Among Women Delivering Live Births: 1992* (NIH Publication No. 96-3819). Washington, DC: U. S. Government Printing Office.

Shiono, P. H. (1996). Prevalence of drug-exposed infants. *Future of Children, 6*(2), 159-163.

Wiemann, C. M., Berenson, A. B., & San Miguel, V. V. (1994). Tobacco, alcohol and illicit drug use among pregnant women: Age and racial/ethnic differences. *Journal of Reproductive Medicine, 39*(10), 769-776.

TOBACCO

Cnattingius, S. (1997). Maternal age modifies the effect of maternal smoking on intrauterine growth retardation but not on late fetal death and placental abruption. *American Journal of Epidemiology, 145*(4), 319-23.

DiFranza, J. R., Lew, R. A. (1995). Effect of maternal cigarette smoking on pregnancy complications and sudden infant death syndrome. *Journal of Family Practice, 40*(4), 385-394.

Hofvendahl, E. A. (1995). Smoking in pregnancy as a risk factor for long-term mortality in the offspring. *Paediatrics & Perinatal Epidemiology, 9*(4), 381-390.

Nordentoft, M., et al. (1996). Intrauterine growth retardation and premature delivery: The influence of maternal smoking and psychosocial factors. *American Journal of Public Health, 86*(3), 347-354.

Oyen, N., Haglund, B., Skjaerven, R., & Irgens, L. M. (1997). Maternal smoking, birthweight and gestational age in sudden infant death syndrome (SIDS) babies and their surviving siblings. *Paediatric & Perinatal Epidemiology, 11* (Supp 1), 84-95.

Samet, J. M., Lewit, E. M., & Warner, K. E. (1994). Involuntary smoking and children's health. *Future of Children, 4*(3), 94-114.

Shu, X. O., Hatch, M. C., Mills, J., Clemens, J., & Susser, M. (1995). Maternal smoking, alcohol drinking, caffeine consumption, and fetal growth: Results from a prospective study. *Epidemiology, 6*(2), 115-120.

TEACHING STRATEGIES, EDUCATIONAL ISSUES

Au, K., & Kawakami, A. (1984) Vygotskian perspectives in discussion processes in small group reading lessons. In P. Peterson, L. Wilkinson, & M. Jallomam (Eds.). *The Social Context of Instruction: Group Organization and Group Processes (pp. 209-225)* Orlando. FL: Academic Press

American Academy of Pediatrics. (1996). Universal access to good-quality education and care of children from birth to 5 years: American Academy of Pediatrics, Committee on Early Childhood, Adoption and Dependent Care. *Pediatrics, 97*(3), 417-419.

Bandura, A (1986) *Social Foundation of Thought and Action: A Social Cognitive Theory.* Englewood Cliffs, NJ Prentice Hall

Berkowitz, I (1993 *Aggression: Its Causes, Consequences and Control.* Philadelphia. Temple Press.

Borkowsky, J., Carr, M., Rellinger, E., & Pressley, M. (1990) Self regulated cognition: Interdependence of metacognition, attributions, and self esteem. In B. Jones & L. Idol (Eds.), *Dimensions in Thinking* (pp. 53-92). Hillsdale, NJ: Erlbaum

Brophy, J. (1996) *Teaching Problem Students* , New York . Guildford Press

Caine, R., & Caine, G., (1994) *Making Connections: Teaching and the Human Brain.* Addison Wesley

Charney, R. (1992) *Teaching Children to Care: Management in the Responsive Classroom.* Greenfield, MA Northeast Foundation for Children

Chernow, F. & Chernow C (1981) *Classroom Discipline and Control 101 Practical Techniques* West Nyack, NY: Parker

Corno, L. (1989), Self regulated learning A Volitional analysis. In B. Zimmereman and D. Schunk (eds.) *Self-Regulated Learning and Academic Achievement,* pp. 111-142. New York: Springer-Verlag.

Crocker, A. C., Lavin, A. T., Palfrey, J. S., Porter, S. M., Shaw, D. M., & Weill, K. S. (1994). Supports for children with HIV infection in school: Best practices guidelines. *Journal of School Health, 64*(1), 33-36.

Evertson, C., Emmer, E., Clements, B., & Worsham, M (1994) *Classroom Management for Elementary Teachers* (3rd ed.) Boston: Allyn & Bacon.

Forrest, D. C. (1994). The cocaine-exposed infant, Part I: Identification and assessment. *Journal of Pediatric Health Care, 8*(1), 3-6.

Forrest, D. C. (1994). The cocaine-exposed infant, Part II: Intervention and teaching. *Journal of Pediatric Health Care, 8*(1), 7-11.

Gardner, H (1983) *Frames of Mind* New York: Basic Books.

Glasser, W (1990) *The Quality School Managing Students Without Coercion.* New York Harper and Row.

Gordon, T. (1970) *Parent effectiveness training.* New York: Wyden.

Gordon, T. (1974) *Teacher Effectiveness Training.* New York: Wyden.

Huffman, D. M., Price, B. K., & Langel, L. (1994). Therapeutic handling techniques for the infant affected by cocaine. *Neonatal Network, 13*(5), 9-13.

Kleinfeld, J.M., Wescott, S. (Eds) 1993 *Fantastic Antone Succeeds! Experiences in Educating Children with Fetal Alcohol Syndrome* Fairbanks, Alaska: University of Alaska Press

Lewin, F. Nelson, R, & Tollefson, N. (1983) Teacher attitudes toward disruptive children. *Elementary School Guidance and Counseling,* 17, 188-189

Maier, N. P. (1995). Examining the feasibility of hospital-based intervention for mothers and their drug-exposed neonates. *Pediatric Nursing, 21*(2), 169-172.

Miller, S. M. (1992). Policy options: Early intervention services for substance-exposed infants. *Journal of Drug Education, 22*(4), 273-281.

Moore, W.L. & Cooper, H (1984) Correlation's between teacher and student background and teacher perceptions of discipline problems and disciplinary techniques. *Psychology in the Schools* 21, 386-392

Pressley, M & Woloshyn, V & Associates (1995) *Cognitive Strategy Instruction that Really Improves Children's Academic Performance* (2nd ed.) MA: Brooklyn Books.

Rogers, C., & Freiberg H.J. (1994) *Freedom to Learn* (3rd ed.) New York: Merril

Schedif, K., (1993) *Helping Students Become Strategic Learners: Guidelines for teaching.* MA: Brookline.

Setley, S., (1995) *Taming the Dragons: Real Help for Real School Problems* St. Louis: Starfish.

Shure, M.B. and Spivack, G. (1988) "Interpersonal Cognitive Problem Solving" in Price,R.H., Cowen, E.L., Lorion, R.P.,Ramos-McKay (editors) *Fourteen Ounces of Prevention.* American Psychological Association: Washinton D.C.

Soodak, L & Bodell, D. (1994) Teachers" thinking about difficult to teach students. *Journal of Educational Research,* 88, 44-51.

Spaulding, R. (1978) Adapting teaching styles to learning styles. *Journal of Classroom Interaction, 14* (1) 10-18.

Vgotsky, L., (1962) *Thought and Language* Cambridge. MA: MIT Press.

Walker, H., McConnell, S. Holmes, D., Todis, B., Walker, J., & Golden, H. (1982) *The Walker Social Skills Program: The ACCEPTS Program.* Austin, TX: Pro-Ed.

Watkins, K. & Durant, L., (1996)*Working with Children and Families Affected by Substance Abuse.* New York. The Center for Applied Research in Education.

Index

U

V

W